Ed She... Ukulele Chord Songbook

Published by
Wise Publications
14-15 Berners Street, London W1T 3LJ, UK.

Exclusive Distributors:
Music Sales Limited
Distribution Centre, Newmarket Road,
Bury St Edmunds, Suffolk IP33 3YB, UK.

Music Sales Pty Limited
4th floor, Lisgar House, 30-32 Carrington Street,
Sydney, NSW 2000, Australia.

Order No. AM1011120
ISBN: 978-1-78558-109-0
This book © Copyright 2015 Wise Publications,
a division of Music Sales Limited.

Compiled and edited by Adrian Hopkins.
Chord diagrams created by Shedwork.com
Original music arranged by Matt Cowe.
Engraved by Paul Ewers Music Design.
Cover designed by Tim Field.
Printed in the EU.

Your Guarantee of Quality:

As publishers, we strive to produce every
book to the highest commercial standards.

This book has been carefully designed
to minimise awkward page turns and to
make playing from it a real pleasure.

Particular care has been given to specifying
acid-free, neutral-sized paper made from pulps
which have not been elemental chlorine bleached.
This pulp is from farmed sustainable forests and
was produced with special regard for the environment.

Throughout, the printing and binding have
been planned to ensure a sturdy, attractive
publication which should give years of enjoyment.
If your copy fails to meet our high standards,
please inform us and we will gladly replace it.

www.musicsales.com

Wise Publications
part of The Music Sales Group
London / New York / Paris / Sydney / Copenhagen /
Berlin / Madrid / Hong Kong / Tokyo

The A Team

Words & Music by Ed Sheeran

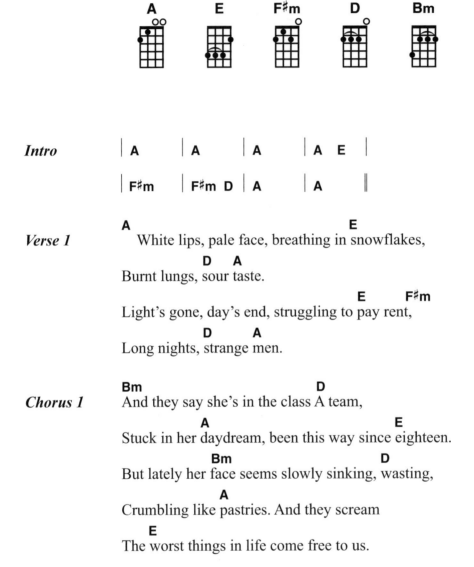

Intro

| A | A | A | A E |
| F#m | F#m D | A | A ‖

Verse 1

   A   E
   White lips, pale face, breathing in snowflakes,

               D   A
Burnt lungs, sour taste.

                            E   F#m
Light's gone, day's end, struggling to pay rent,

              D   A
Long nights, strange men.

Chorus 1

  Bm   D
And they say she's in the class A team,

             A   E
Stuck in her daydream, been this way since eighteen.

              Bm   D
But lately her face seems slowly sinking, wasting,

            A
Crumbling like pastries. And they scream

   E
The worst things in life come free to us.

                              F#m   D
cont.   'Cause we're just under the upper hand
                 A
                    And go mad for a couple grams,
                 F#m   D   A
                    And she don't want to go outside   tonight.
                         F#m   D
                 And in a pipe she flies to the Motherland
                 A
                    Or sells love to another man.
                          F#m   A   E   F#m   D A
                    It's too cold   outside   for angels to fly,
                         F#m   D A
                 Angels to fly.

                 A   E   F#m
Verse 2   Ripped gloves, raincoat, tried to swim and stay afloat,
                         D   A
                 Dry house, wet clothes.

                                              E   F#m
                 Loose change, bank notes, weary-eyed, dry throat,
                         D   A
                 Call girl, no phone.

                 Bm   D
Chorus 2   And they say she's in the class A team,
                        A   E
                 Stuck in her daydream, been this way since eighteen.
                        Bm   D
                 But lately her face seems slowly sinking, wasting,
                       A
                 Crumbling like pastries. And they scream
                      E
                 The worst things in life come free to us.
                         F#m   D
                 'Cause we're just under the upper hand
                 A
                    And go mad for a couple grams,
                 F#m   D   A
                    And she don't want to go outside   tonight.

cont.

       F♯m   **D**
And in a pipe she flies to the Motherland

A
  Or sells love to another man.

F♯m   **D**   **A**   **Bm**
  It's too cold   outside   for angels to fly.

Bridge

Bm   **D**   **F♯m**
That angel will die covered in white,

           A
Closed eye and hoping for a better life.

Bm   **D**
This time, we'll fade out tonight,

              (F♯m)
Straight down the line.

Instrumental ‖: **F♯m** | **D** | **A** | **A** :‖

Chorus 3

Bm   **D**
And they say she's in the class A team,

      A   **E**
Stuck in her daydream, been this way since eighteen.

          Bm   **D**
But lately her face seems slowly sinking, wasting,

         A
Crumbling like pastries. And they scream

    E
The worst things in life come free to us.

         F♯m   **D**
And we're all under the upper hand

A
  And go mad for a couple grams,

F♯m   **D**   **A**
  And we don't want to go outside   tonight.

cont.

F♯m   D
And in the pipe fly to the Motherland

A
 Or sell love to another man.

F♯m   D A E   F♯m D A
 It's too cold outside for angels to fly,

     F♯m D A
Angels to fly,___

    F♯m D A
To fly,___ fly,___

      F♯m D A
For angels to fly, to fly, to fly,

E   A
Angels to die.

Afire Love

Words & Music by Ed Sheeran, Johnny McDaid,
Foy Vance & Christophe Beck

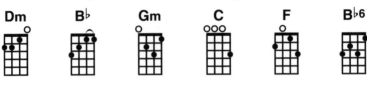

Intro ‖: Dm | B♭ | Gm | C :‖ *Play 3 times*

Verse 1

Dm
    Things were all good yesterday,

                                     B♭
And then the devil took your memory.

And if you fell to your death today,
                           Dm
I hope that heaven is your resting place.
                             F
I heard the doctor put your chest in pain,
                               Gm
But then that could've been the medicine.
                          C
And now you're lying in the bed again,
                             B♭
Either way I'll cry with the rest of them.

Pre-chorus 1

B♭   F   Dm
And my father told me, son,
         B♭   F
It's not his fault he doesn't know your face.
B♭   F   Dm
And you're not the only one,
         B♭   C
Although my grandma used to say

He used to sing:

Chorus 1

    Dm   B♭   B♭6

Darling, hold me in your arms the way you did last night,

                   C

And we'll lie in - side for a little while, here, oh.

Dm   B♭   B♭6

I could look into your eyes until the sun comes up,

                       C   Dm

And we're wrapped in light, in life, and love.

                       B♭   B♭6

Put your open lips on mine and slowly let them shut,

               C

For they're de - signed to be together, oh.

Dm   B♭   B♭6

With your body next to mine our hearts will beat as one,

                   C   Dm

And we're set a - light, we're afire love.

Link | Dm | B♭ | Gm | C ||

Verse 2

    Dm

Things were all good yesterday,

                            B♭

Then the devil took your breath a - way.

And now we're left with the pain,

Black suit, black tie, standing in the rain.

Dm   F

And now my family is one again,

                                            Gm

Stapled all together with the strangers and a friend.

                                       C

Came to my mind, I should paint it with a pen,

Six years old, I remember when.

Pre-chorus 2   As Pre-chorus 1

Chorus 2   As Chorus 1

Bridge

Dm   B♭   B♭6
    Love,＿ love.

                                                    C
It's in the love, the love, the love, the love.

Dm   B♭
  It's in the love, the love, the love, the love.

B♭6   C
  It's in the love, the love, the love, the love.

         Dm   B♭
And my father and all of my family

              B♭6   C
Rise from these seats to sing "Hallelu - jah."

         Dm   B♭
And my mother and all of my family

              B♭6   C
Rise from these seats to sing "Hallelu - jah."

         Dm   B♭
And my brother and all of my family

              B♭6   C
Rise from these seats to sing "Hallelu - jah."

         Dm   B♭
And my father and all of my family

              B♭6   C
Rise from these seats to sing "Hallelu - jah."

Dm B♭ B♭6   C
      It's in the love, the love, the love, the love.

Dm   B♭
  It's in the love, the love, the love, the love.

B♭6   C
  It's in the love, the love, the love, the love.

Outro   ‖: Dm | B♭ | B♭6 | C   :‖ *Play 3 times*

10

Bloodstream

Words & Music by Ed Sheeran, Gary Lightbody,
Johnny McDaid, Kesi Dryden, Piers Aggett & Amir Izadkhah

Dsus4 Bb6 Csus4 G7

To match original recording, tune ukulele up one semitone

Intro

Dsus4   Bb6   Csus4   G7
   Na, na, na, na, mmm, mmm.

Dsus4   Bb6   Csus4   G7
Mmm,__ mmm,____ mmm.__

Dsus4   Bb6   Csus4   G7
Mmm,__ mmm,____ mmm.__

Verse 1

Dsus4   Bb6
  I've been spinning out of time,   couple women by my side,

Csus4   G7
  I got sinning on my mind,   sipping on red wine.

Dsus4   Bb6   Csus4
  I've been sitting here for a - ges ripping out the pa - ges,

       G7
How'd I get so faded, how'd I get so faded?

Pre-chorus 1

Dsus4   Bb6
Oh, no, no, don't leave me lonely now,

   Csus4   G7
If you loved me how'd you never learn?

Dsus4   Bb6
Ooh, coloured crimson in my eyes,

          Csus4   G7
One or two could free my mind.

Chorus 1

B♭6   Csus4   Dsus4
   This is how it ends,

                  B♭6   Csus4   G7
I feel the chemicals burn in my   bloodstream.

B♭6   Csus4   Dsus4
  Fading out again,

                  B♭6   Csus4   G7
I feel the chemicals burn in my   bloodstream.

N.C.   Dsus4   B♭6   Csus4   G7
So tell me when it kicks in, mmm,___ mmm,_____ mmm.___

                      Dsus4   B♭6   Csus4   G7
Well, tell me when it kicks in, mmm,___ mmm,_____ mmm.___

Verse 2

Dsus4   B♭6   Csus4
   I've been looking for a lov - er, thought I'd find her in a bot - tle,

                   G7
God, make me another one,   I'll be feeling this tomorrow.

Dsus4   B♭6
Lord, forgive me for the things I've done,

                      Csus4
I was never meant to hurt no one,

               G7
And I saw scars upon a   broken-hearted lover.

Pre-chorus 2 As Pre-chorus 1

Chorus 2   As Chorus 1

Bridge

(G7)
Well, tell me when it kicks in.

B♭6   Csus4   Dsus4   B♭6
  All the voices in my mind calling out across the line.

          Csus4   Dsus4   B♭6
All the voices in my mind calling out across the line.

           Csus4   Dsus4   B♭6
‖: All the voices in my mind calling out across the line.

          Csus4   Dsus4   B♭6
All the voices in my mind calling out across the line. :‖

  Csus4   Dsus4   B♭6
‖: Tell me when it kicks in,   and I saw scars upon her.

Csus4   Dsus4   B♭6
Tell me when it kicks in,   broken - hearted. :‖ *Play 4 times*

Outro

B♭6 Csus4   Dsus4   B♭6
Tell me when it kicks in,   and I saw scars upon her.

Csus4   Dsus4   B♭6
Tell me when it kicks in,   broken - hearted.

Csus4   Dsus4   B♭6
Tell me when it kicks in,   and I saw scars upon her.

Csus4   Dsus4   N.C.
Tell me when it kicks in,   broken - hearted.

All Of The Stars

Words & Music by Ed Sheeran & Johnny McDaid

E   B   G#m   F#   Bmaj7

Verse 1

  E   B   G#m B   E
    It's just another night   and I'm sta - ring   at the moon,
B   F#
    I saw a shooting star   and thought of you.
E   B   G#m B   E
    I sang a lullaby   by the wa - ter - side and knew
B   F#
    If you were here, I'd sing to you.
E   B   G#m B   E   B
    You're on the other side   as the sky - line splits in two,
                 F#
Miles away from seeing you.
E   B   G#m B   E
    But I can see the stars   from A - me - ri - ca,
B   F#
    I wonder, do you see them too?

Chorus 1

N.C.   B
So open your eyes and see
            F#
The way our ho - rizons meet.
          G#m
And all of the lights will lead
         E
Into the night with me.
        B
And I know these scars will bleed,
       F#
But both of our hearts believe
        G#m   E   B   F#
All of these stars will guide___ us home.

Link ‖ B | B   ‖

Verse 2

E   B   G#m B   E
   I can hear your heart   on the ra - di - o beat,

B   F#
   They're playing "Chasing Cars" and I thought of us.

E   B   G#m B E
   Back to the time   you were ly - ing next to me

B   F#
   I looked across and fell in love.

E   B   G#m   B E
   So I took your hand   back through lamp - lit streets and knew

B   F#
   Everything led back to you.

E   B   G#m B   E
   So can you see the   stars over Am - ster - dam,

B   F#
   Hear the song my heart is beating to?

Chorus 2   As Chorus 1

Outro

    E   F#
And oh,___

    G#m Bmaj⁷
And oh,____

    E   F# B
And oh,____

E   B   G#m B   E
   I can see the stars   from A - me - ri - ca.

Autumn Leaves

Words & Music by Ed Sheeran & Jake Gosling

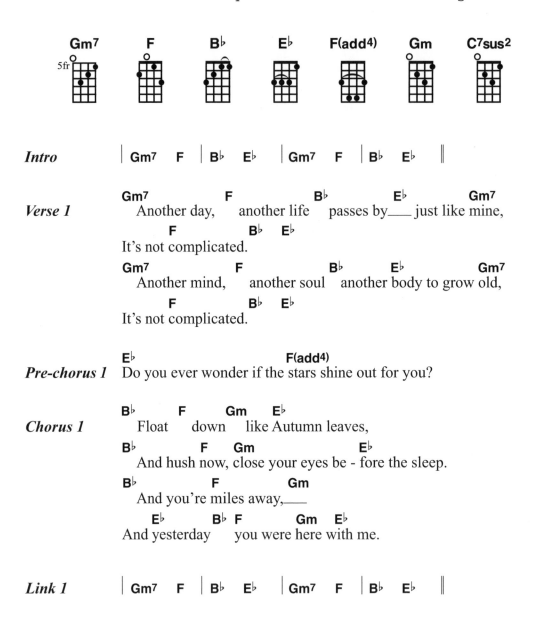

Gm7   **F**   **B♭**   **E♭**   **F(add4)**   **Gm**   **C7sus2**

Intro | Gm7 F | B♭ E♭ | Gm7 F | B♭ E♭ ‖

Verse 1

Gm7   F   B♭   E♭   Gm7
Another day,   another life   passes by___ just like mine,
     F   B♭   E♭
It's not complicated.

Gm7   F   B♭   E♭   Gm7
Another mind,   another soul   another body to grow old,
     F   B♭   E♭
It's not complicated.

Pre-chorus 1

E♭   F(add4)
Do you ever wonder if the stars shine out for you?

Chorus 1

B♭   F   Gm   E♭
Float   down   like Autumn leaves,
B♭   F   Gm   E♭
And hush now, close your eyes be - fore the sleep.
B♭   F   Gm
And you're miles away,___
     E♭   B♭ F   Gm   E♭
And yesterday   you were here with me.

Link 1 | Gm7 F | B♭ E♭ | Gm7 F | B♭ E♭ ‖

Verse 2

Gm7   F   Bb   Eb   Gm7
Another tear,   another cry,   another place for us to die,

        F   Bb Eb
It's not complicated.

Gm7   F   Bb   Eb   Gm7
Another life that's gone to waste, another light lost from your face,

        F   Bb Eb
It's complicated.

Pre-chorus 2

Eb   F(add4)
Is it that it's over or do   birds still sing for you?

Chorus 2   As Chorus 1

Bridge

C7sus2   Eb
Ooh, how I miss you,

    Bb   F
My symphony played the song that carried you out.

C7sus2   Eb
Ooh, how I miss you,

    Bb   F
And I,   I miss you and I wish you'd stay.

Pre-chorus 3   As Pre-chorus 1

Chorus 3   As Chorus 1

Link 2

Gm7   F   Bb   Eb
Ooh, ooh,   ooh, ooh,   ooh, ooh,   ooh, ooh.

Gm7   F   Bb   Eb
Ooh, ooh,   ooh, ooh,   ooh, ooh,   ooh, ooh.

Outro

Bb   F   Gm   Eb
Touch   down   like a seven four seven,

Bb   F   Gm   C7sus2
We'll stay   out   and we'll live forever now.

The City

Words & Music by Ed Sheeran & Jake Gosling

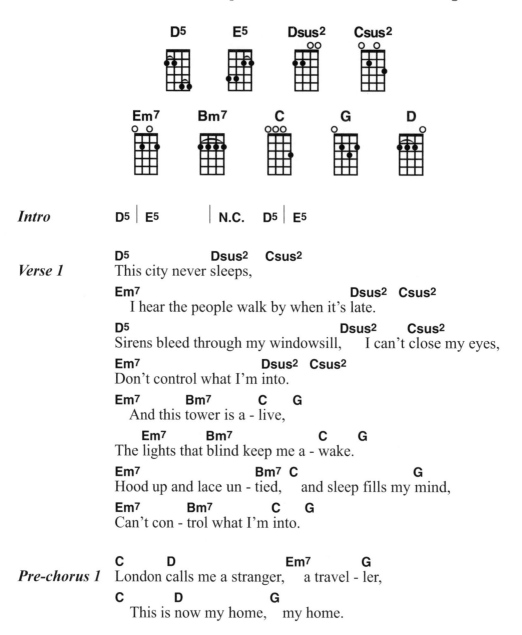

Intro   D5 | E5 | N.C. D5 | E5

       D5   Dsus2 Csus2

Verse 1 This city never sleeps,

       Em7   Dsus2 Csus2

        I hear the people walk by when it's late.

       D5   Dsus2 Csus2

       Sirens bleed through my windowsill, I can't close my eyes,

       Em7   Dsus2 Csus2

       Don't control what I'm into.

       Em7   Bm7   C G

        And this tower is a - live,

         Em7   Bm7   C G

       The lights that blind keep me a - wake.

       Em7   Bm7 C   G

       Hood up and lace un - tied, and sleep fills my mind,

       Em7   Bm7   C G

       Can't con - trol what I'm into.

       C   D   Em7   G

Pre-chorus 1 London calls me a stranger, a travel - ler,

       C   D   G

        This is now my home, my home.

Chorus 1

Em7 Bm7 C   G
            I'm burning on the back street,

Em7 Bm7 C   G
          Stuck here sitting in the back seat.

Em7 Bm7 C   G
        I'm blazing on the street,

Em7   Bm7
What I do isn't up to you,

      C   G
If the city never sleeps then that makes two.

Link 1   D5 | E5 | N.C.   D5 | E5

Verse 2

Em7   Bm7   C   G
   The pavement is my___ friend,

Em7   Bm7   C G
   It will take me where I need to go.

Em7   Bm7 C   G
I find it trips me up   and puts me down,

Em7 Bm7   C   G
This is not what I'm used to.

Em7   Bm7   C   G
   And the shop across the road

Em7   Bm7   C   G
   Fills my needs and gives me company when I need it.

Em7   Bm7
Voices speak through my walls,

C   G   Bm7   C G
   I don't think I'm gonna make it past to - morrow.___

Pre-chorus 2   As Pre-chorus 1

Chorus 2   As Chorus 1

Bridge

```
    Em                      G
      And my lungs hurt    and my ears bled
    Am                            C
      With the sound of the city life    echoed in my head.
    Em                G
      Do I need this    to keep me alive?
    Am                            C
    The traffic stops and starts but I    need to move along.
```

Chorus 3

```
    C         D                    Em7  G
      London calls me a stranger,____
    C            D       G
      And this is not my home, home.
```

Chorus 4   As Chorus 1

Everything Has Changed

Words & Music by Ed Sheeran & Taylor Swift

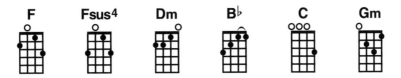

To match original recording, tune ukulele up one semitone

Intro 　|: F　　　| F Fsus⁴ | F　　　| F Fsus⁴ :||

Verse 1

　　　　　F　　Dm　　　　　　　　　　　B♭
　　　　All I knew this morning when I woke
　　　　　　　　　　　　　　　C
　　　　Is I know something now,　know something now I didn't before.
　　　　F　　　　　　Dm　　　　　　　　　　　B♭
　　　　And all I've seen since eighteen hours ago

　　　　Is green eyes and freckles and your smile
　　　　　　C
　　　　In the back of my mind making me feel like.

Pre-chorus 1

　　　　　F
　　　　I just wanna know you better,
　　　　　Gm
　　　　Know　　you better, know you better now.
　　　　B♭
　　　　I just wanna know you better,
　　　　　　　Dm　　　　　C
　　　　Know　　you better, know　you better now.
　　　　F
　　　　I just wanna know you better,
　　　　　　Gm
　　　　Know　　you better, know you better now.
　　　　B♭　　　　　　　　　　Dm　　C
　　　　I just wanna know you, know you, know you.

Chorus 1

(C)   F
'Cause all I know is we said hello

        Dm
And your eyes look like coming home,

  C   B♭
All I know is a simple name,   everything has changed.

F   Dm
All I know is you held the door, you'll be mine and I'll be yours,

  C   B♭
All I know since yesterday   is everything has changed.

Link

| F | F Fsus4 | F | F Fsus4 ‖

Verse 2

F   Dm   B♭
  And all my walls stood tall painted blue,

                     C
And I'll take 'em down, take 'em down and open up the door for you

F   Dm   B♭
  And all I feel in my stomach is butterflies,

The beautiful kind, making up for lost time,

C
Taking flight, making me feel right like.

Pre-chorus 2 As Pre-chorus 1

Chorus 2   As Chorus 1

Bridge

Dm   B♭
  Come back and tell me why,

                     F   C
I'm feeling like I've missed you all this time.___

Dm   B♭
  And meet me there to - night

                     F   C
And let me know that it's not all in my mind.

Pre-chorus 3   **F**
           I just wanna know you better,

              Dm
           Know   you better, know you better now.

           B♭   **Dm**   **C**
           I just wanna know you, know you, know you.

Chorus 3   As Chorus 1

           F   **Dm**
Chorus 4   All I know is we said, hello,   so dust off your highest hopes,

           C   **B♭**
           All I know is pouring rain   and everything has changed.

           F   **Dm**
           All I know is a new found grace, all my days I'll know your face,

           C   **B♭**   **N.C.**
           All I know since yesterday   is   everything has changed.

Don't

Words & Music by Ed Sheeran, Ali Jones-Muhammad,
Raphael Saadiq, Benjamin Levin, Conesha Owens & Dawn Robinson

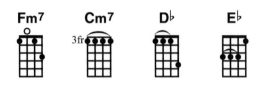

Intro

N.C.
Ah, la-n-la-la.

| Fm⁷ | Cm⁷ | D♭ | E♭ | |

| Fm⁷ | Cm⁷ | D♭ | N.C. ‖

        Ah, la-n-la-la.

Verse 1

    Fm⁷   Cm⁷
I met this girl late last year,
        D♭   E♭
She said: "Don't you worry if I disappear."
         Fm⁷   Cm⁷
I told her: "I'm not really looking for another mistake."
       D♭   E♭
I called an old friend thinking that the trouble would wait.
        Fm⁷   Cm⁷
But then I jump right in, a week later returned,
       D♭   E♭
I reckon she was only looking for a lover to burn.
      Fm⁷   Cm⁷
But I gave her my time for two or three nights,
        D♭   E♭
Then I put it on pause until the moment was right.

cont.

          Fm⁷   **Cm⁷**   **D♭**   **E♭**
I went a - way, four months un - til our paths crossed a - gain,
           Fm⁷   **Cm⁷**
She told me: "I was never looking for a friend,
               D♭   **E♭**
Maybe you could swing by my room around ten.
           Fm⁷   **Cm⁷**
Baby, bring the lemon and a bottle of gin,
              D♭   **E♭**
We'll be inbetween the sheets till the late A.M."
             Fm⁷   **Cm⁷**
Baby, if you wanted me then you should've just said,
           D♭   **E♭**
She's singing. (Ah, la-n-la-la.)

Chorus 1

          (E♭)   **Fm⁷**   **Cm⁷**   **D♭**
Don't fuck with my love, that heart is so cold,
      E♭   **Fm⁷**   **Cm⁷**   **D♭**   **E♭**
All over my home, I don't wanna know that, babe. (Ah, la-n-la-la.)
        (E♭)   **Fm⁷** **Cm⁷**   **D♭**
Don't fuck with my love, I told her she knows,
      E♭   **Fm⁷**   **Cm⁷**
Take aim and re - load, I don't wanna know that, babe.
D♭   **E♭**
(Ah, la-n-la-la.)

Verse 2

(E♭)   **Fm⁷**   **Cm⁷**
And for a couple weeks I only want to see her,
              D♭   **E♭**
We drink away the days with a take-away pizza.
          Fm⁷   **Cm⁷**
Before, a text message was the only way to reach her,
              D♭   **E♭**
Now she's staying at my place and loves the way I treat her.
          Fm⁷   **Cm⁷**
Singing out A - retha, all over the track like a feature,
      D♭   **E♭**
And never wants to sleep, I guess that I don't want to either.
Fm⁷   **Cm⁷**
   But me and her, we make money the same way,
D♭   **E♭**
Four cities, two planes, the same day.

25

cont.

Fm⁷   Cm⁷
And those shows have never been what it's about,
      D♭   E♭
But maybe we'll go together and just figure it out.
         Fm⁷   Cm⁷
I'd rather put on a film with you and sit on the couch,
         D♭   E♭
But we should get on a plane or we'll be missing it now.
         Fm⁷   Cm⁷
Wish I'd have written it out, the way that things played out,
         D♭   E♭
When she was kissing him, how I was con - fused about.
          Fm⁷   Cm⁷
Now she should figure it out while I'm sat here singing:
D♭   E♭
(Ah, la-n-la-la.)

Chorus 2   As Chorus 1

Verse 3

Fm⁷   Cm⁷
(Knock, knock, knock) On my hotel door
D♭   E♭
I don't even know if she knows what for.
         Fm⁷   Cm⁷
She was crying on my shoulder, I already told ya,
D♭   E♭
Trust and respect is what we do this for.
Fm⁷   Cm⁷
I never intended to be next,
         D♭   E♭
But you didn't need to take him to bed, that's all.
Fm⁷   Cm⁷
And I never saw him as a threat,
         D♭   E♭
Until you disappeared with him to have sex, of course.
Fm⁷   Cm⁷
It's not like we were both on tour,
         D♭   E♭
We were staying on the same hotel floor.
         Fm⁷   Cm⁷
And I wasn't looking for a promise or com - mitment,
         D♭   E♭
It was never just fun and I thought you were different.

cont.

Fm⁷   Cm⁷
This is not the way you rea - lise what you wanted,

        D♭   E♭
It's a bit too much, too late if I'm honest.

        Fm⁷   Cm⁷
And all this time God knows I'm singing:

D♭   E♭
(Ah, la-n-la-la.)

Chorus 3   As Chorus 1

                (E♭)   Fm⁷   Cm⁷   D♭
Chorus 4   Don't fuck with my love, that heart is so cold,

        E♭   Fm⁷   Cm⁷   D♭   E♭
All over my home, I don't wanna know that, babe. (Ah, la-n-la-la.)

                (E♭)   Fm⁷   Cm⁷   D♭
Don't fuck with my love, I told her she knows,

        E♭   Fm⁷   Cm⁷
Take aim and re - load, I don't wanna know that, babe.

N.C.
(Ah, la-n-la-la.)

Even My Dad Does Sometimes

Words & Music by Ed Sheeran & Amy Wadge

D   A   G   Bm

Intro

| D | A G | D | A G ‖

Verse 1

```
    D                    A        G          D      A G
It's all right to cry,   even my dad does some - times,
    D                      A      G          D      A G
So don't wipe your eyes,   tears re - mind you you're a - live.
    D                        A         G           D      A G
It's all right to die 'cause death's the only thing you haven't tried,
    D               A G         D A G
But just for tonight     hold on.
```

Chorus 1

```
    D                      G
So live life like you're giving up
    D                    G
'Cause you act like you are.
    D               G
Go ahead and just live it up,
Bm          A            G
Go on and tear me apart.
```

Verse 2

```
    D                    A       G          D      A G
It's all right to shake,   even my hand does some - times,
    D              A       G        D      A G
So inside we rage    against the dying of the light.
    D                  A          G           D      A G
It's all right to say that death's the only thing you haven't tried,
    D             A G        D A G
But just for today___ hold on.___
```

Chorus 2

D   G
    So live life like you're giving up

D   G
    'Cause you act like you are.

D   G
    Go ahead and just live it up,

Bm   A   G
    Go on and tear me apart,   hold on.

Instrumental ‖: D | G | D | G   :‖ *Play 4 times*

Chorus 3

D   G
    Live life like you're giving up

D   G
    'Cause you act like you are.

D   G
    Go ahead and just live it up,

Bm   A   G
    Go on and tear me apart   and hold on.

Drunk

Words & Music by Ed Sheeran & Jake Gosling

| G | Gmaj7 | Em7 | C(add9) | D | Am7 | Em |

Verse 1

G
   I wanna be drunk when I wake up
       Gmaj7   **Em7**
On the right side of the   wrong bed,

And never an excuse I made up,
                 C(add9)
Tell you the truth I hate what   didn't kill me,
               D   **G**
It never made me strong - er at all.

Love will scar your make-up, lips sticks to me,
   Gmaj7   **Em7**
So now I maybe lean back there.
                      C(add9)
I'm sat here wishing I was sober,____
                  D   **G**
I know I'll never hold you like I used to.____

Pre-chorus 1

(G) **Em7**   **D**
But a house gets cold when you   cut the heating,
G   **C(add9)**
Without you to hold   I'll be freezing.
Em7   **D**
   Can't rely on my heart to beat in,
G   **C(add9)**
'Cause you take parts of it every evening.
Em7   **D**
Take words out of my mouth just from breathing,
G   **C(add9)**   **G**
Replace with phrases like "When you leaving me?"

Chorus 1

G   Am⁷   C   Em   G
Should I, should I? Maybe I'll get drunk a - gain.

        Em   G   Em   G   C   D
I'll be drunk a - gain, I'll be drunk a - gain to feel a little love.___

Verse 2

G
I wanna hold your heart in both hands,

                              Gmaj⁷   Em⁷
Not watch it fizzle at the bottom of a Coke can.

And I got no plans for the weekend,

So should we speak then, keep it between friends?

C(add⁹)   D   G
Though I know you'll never love me like you used to.

There may be other people like us,

                         Gmaj⁷
Who see the flicker a Clipper when they light up.

Em⁷   C(add⁹)
Flames just create us but burns don't heal like be - fore,

                     D   G
And you don't hold me any - more.___

Pre-chorus 2

      Em⁷   D
On cold days cold plays out like the band's name,

G   C(add⁹)
I know I can't heal things with a handshake.

Em⁷   D
You know I can change   as I began saying,

G   C(add⁹)
You cut me wide open like landscape.

Em⁷   D
Open bottles of beer but never champagne,

G   C(add⁹)
To applaud you with the sound that my hands make.

Chorus 2   As Chorus 1

Bridge

Em7   G

All by my - self, I'm here again.

Em7   G

All by my - self, you know I'll never change.

Em   G   C(add9)   Em

All by my - self,   all by my - self.

Chorus 3

                    G   Em   G

I'm just drunk a - gain, I'll be   drunk a - gain,

        Em   G   C   D

I'll be   drunk a - gain to feel a little love.___

Give Me Love

Words & Music by Ed Sheeran, Christopher Leonard & Jake Gosling

Am   F   C   Dm   G   Fmaj7

To match original recording, tune ukulele up one semitone

Intro ‖: Am | F | C | C :‖ *Play 4 times*

Verse 1

Am   F   C
Give me love   like her,

Am   F   C
'Cause lately I've been waking up alone.

Am   F   C
Paint splattered teardrops on my shirt,

Am   F   C
Told you I'd let them go.

Pre-chorus 1

(C)   Dm
And that I'll fight my corner,

            F
Maybe to - night I'll call ya

       C   G/B   G
After my blood turns into alcohol,

     Dm   F
No, I just wanna hold ya.

Chorus 1

C   Dm   Fmaj7
Give a little time to me or burn this out,

C   Dm   Fmaj7
We'll play hide and seek to turn this around,

C   Dm   Fmaj7
All I want is the taste that your lips allow.

cont.

    Am   G   Fmaj⁷

My, my,   my, my,___ oh give me love.

  (Am)   (F)   (C)

My, my,   my, my,___ oh give me love.

  (Am)   (F)   (C)

My, my,   my, my,___ oh give me love.

  (Am)   (F)   (C)

My, my,   my, my,___ oh give me love.

  (Am)   (F)   (C)

My, my,   my, my,___ give me love.

Verse 2

  Am   F   C

Give me love like never before,

  Am   F   C

'Cause lately I've been craving more.

  Am   F   C

And it's been a while but   I still feel the same,

  Am   F   C

Maybe I should let you go.

Pre-chorus 2

  (C)   Dm

You know I'll fight my corner

              F

And that to - night I'll call ya

         C   G/B G

After my blood is drowning in alcohol,

    Dm   F

No, I just wanna hold ya.

Chorus 2

  C   Dm   Fmaj⁷

Give a little time to me or burn this out,

  C   Dm   Fmaj⁷

We'll play hide and seek to turn this around,

  C   Dm   Fmaj⁷

All I want is the taste that your lips allow.

  Am   G   Fmaj⁷

My, my,   my, my,___ oh give me love.

  C   D   Fmaj⁷

Give a little time to me or burn this out,

  C   D   Fmaj⁷

We'll play hide and seek to turn this around,

  C   D   Fmaj⁷

All I want is the taste that your lips allow.

cont.

Am   G   Fmaj⁷
My, my,   my, my,____ oh give me love.

Am   F   C
My, my,   my, my,___ oh give me love.

Am   F   C
My, my,   my, my,___ oh give me love.

Am   F   C
My, my,   my, my,___ oh give me love.

Am   F   C
My, my,   my, my,___ oh give me love.

Bridge

Am   G   Am
‖: M-my my, m-my my, m-my my, give me love, lov - er.

                          G   Am
M-my my, m-my my, m-my my, give me love, lov - er.

                          G   Am
M-my my, m-my my, m-my my, give me love, lov - er.

                          G   Am
M-my my, m-my my, m-my my, give me love, lov - er. :‖ *Play 4 times*

Outro

Am   F
‖:   My, my, my, my,____ oh give me love.

C
My, my, my, my, oh give me love.

Am   F
My, my, my, my,____ oh give me love.

C
My, my, my, my, oh give me love. :‖ *Play 3 times*

Gold Rush

Words & Music by Ed Sheeran & Amy Wadge

E   F♯m   A   C♯m   B

Intro

| E | F♯m | A | A |

| E | F♯m | A | A |

Verse 1

```
 E       F♯m              A
Smoke  alarm went off at nine,
 E                    F♯m        A
I woke up, wiped the sleep out of my eye.
 E             F♯m         A
She left a note,    I'll be back in five,
 E              F♯m          A
Well, I'm still waiting for that moment to arrive, hey.
```

Pre-chorus 1

```
C♯m     A      B
   I was told to put my job in front of you,
C♯m     A           B
But it won't hold me like you do.
```

Chorus 1

```
N.C.              E                F♯m
But I do it for the love, waiting on the gold rush,
            A
Keep it on the edge, smoking on a roll up.
                 E              F♯m
When I see my friends, all they say is hold up
       A
And re - member the time
                 E              F♯m
When we were in school listening to grown-ups.
          A
Didn't learn a thing but then again, you know what,
                 E        F♯m              A
You know how to sing, but you don't know anything other than that.
```

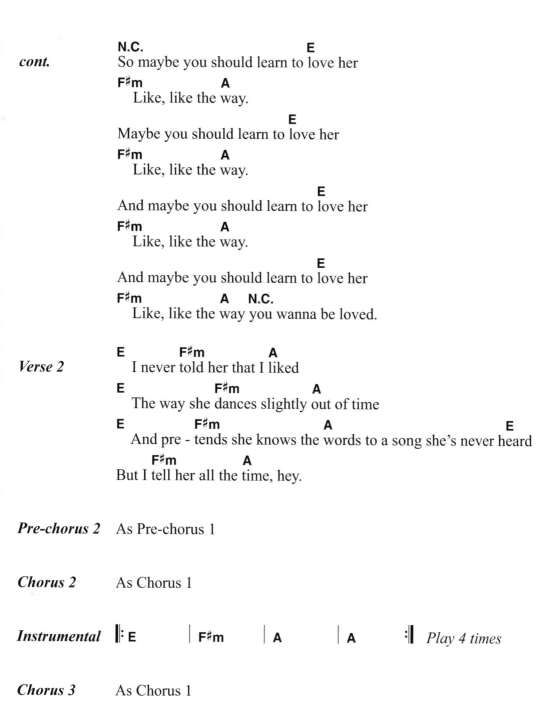

cont.

       N.C.   **E**
So maybe you should learn to love her
F♯m   **A**
  Like, like the way.

                           E
Maybe you should learn to love her
F♯m   **A**
  Like, like the way.

                           E
And maybe you should learn to love her
F♯m   **A**
  Like, like the way.

                           E
And maybe you should learn to love her
F♯m   **A**   **N.C.**
  Like, like the way you wanna be loved.

Verse 2

  E   **F♯m**   **A**
  I never told her that I liked
  E   **F♯m**   **A**
  The way she dances slightly out of time
  E   **F♯m**   **A**   **E**
  And pre - tends she knows the words to a song she's never heard
        F♯m   **A**
But I tell her all the time, hey.

Pre-chorus 2   As Pre-chorus 1

Chorus 2   As Chorus 1

Instrumental ‖: **E** | **F♯m** | **A** | **A**   :‖ *Play 4 times*

Chorus 3   As Chorus 1

Grade 8

Words & Music by Ed Sheeran, Robert Conlon & Sukhdeep Uppal

Gm   B♭   E♭   D   D7

Verse 1

Gm   B♭   E♭   D
My mind is a warrior,   my heart is a foreig - ner,
Gm   B♭   E♭   D
My eyes are the colour of red like a sun - set.
Gm   B♭   E♭   D
I'll never keep it bottled up   and left to the hands of the co - roner,
Gm   B♭   E♭   D
Be a true heart not a follower,   we're not done yet.

Pre-chorus 1

Gm   B♭   E♭
And I see it in your movements tonight,
                          D
If we should ever do this right,
Gm   B♭   E♭   D
I'm never gonna let you down,   oh, I'll never let you down.
Gm   B♭   E♭
And I'm keeping on the down low
                            D
And I'll keep you around so I'll know
Gm   B♭   E♭   D
That I'll never let you down,   I'll never let you down.

Chorus 1

(D)   Gm   B♭
You're strumming on my heart strings like you were a grade eight,
E♭
But I've never felt this way.
        D7   Gm   B♭   E♭
I'll pick your feet up off of the ground and never ever let you down.
D7   Gm   B♭
Now, you're strumming on my heart strings like you were a grade eight,
E♭
But I've never felt this way,
        D7   Gm   B♭   E♭   D7
I'll pick your feet up off of the ground and never ever let you down.

	(D7) **Gm** **B♭** **E♭** **D**

Verse 2

         (D7)   **Gm**   **B♭**   **E♭**   **D**
Now, my eyes are a river filler,   this drink is a liver killer,

       Gm   **B♭**   **E♭**   **D**
  My chest is a pillow for your weary head to lay to rest a - gain.

       Gm   **B♭**   **E♭**   **D**   **Gm**
  Your body is my ballpoint pen and your mind is my new best friend,

                  B♭   **E♭**   **D**
Your eyes are the mirror to take me to the edge again.

Pre-chorus 2   As Pre-chorus 1

Chorus 2   As Chorus 1

Bridge

       Gm   **B♭**   **E♭**   **D**   **Gm**   **B♭**   **E♭**
Hold my heart to stop me bleeding now,   now,   now,

                                     D
And I'll never let you down.

       Gm   **B♭**   **E♭**   **D**   **Gm**   **B♭**   **E♭**
Hold my heart to stop me bleeding now,   now,   now,

                                     D
And I'll never let you down.

       Gm   **B♭**   **E♭**   **D**   **Gm**   **B♭**   **E♭**
Hold my heart to stop me bleeding now,   now,   now,

                                     D
And I'll never let you down.

       Gm   **B♭**   **E♭**   **D**   **Gm**   **B♭**   **E♭**
Hold my heart to stop me bleeding now,   now,   now,

       N.C.
And I'll never let you down.

Chorus 3   As Chorus 1

Outro | **Gm** | **B♭** | **E♭** | **E♭**   **D7** ‖

I'm A Mess

Words & Music by Ed Sheeran

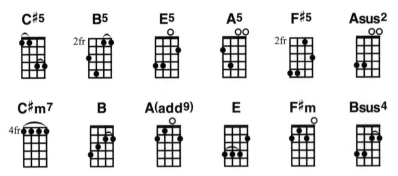

To match original recording, tune ukulele down one semitone

Verse 1

       N.C.   C#5   B5
Oh, I'm a mess right now, inside out,

                 E5
Searching for a sweet surrender,

  A5   E5
But this is not the end.

    F#5 C#5   B5
I can't work it out how___

             E5
Going through the motions,

A5   B5
Going through us.

Pre-chorus 1

  A5   E5
And, oh, I've known it for the longest time

        B5   A5
And all of my hopes, all of my own words

              E5
Are all overwritten on the signs,

          B5
But you're on my road,

     Asus2
Walking me home, home, home, home, home.

Chorus 1

C#m7   B
   See the flames inside my eyes,

         A(add9)   E   F#5
It burns so bright I wanna feel your love, no.____

C#m7   B
   Easy baby, maybe I'm a liar,

        A(add9)   E
But for to - night I wanna fall in love

         F#m   A(add9)
And put your faith in my stomach.

Verse 2

N.C.   C#5   B5
I messed it up this time, late last night.

              E5
Drinking to sup - press devotion

   A5   E5
With fingers inter - twined.

  F#5 C#5   B5
I can't shake this feeling now,____

               E
We're going through the motions,

Asus2   B5
Hoping you'd stop.

Pre-chorus 2

   Asus2
And oh, I've only caused you pain,

 E   B5   A5
I know but all of my words will always below

         E
Of all the love you spoke,

       B5
When you're on my road,

     Asus2
Walking me home, home, home, home, home.

Chorus 2   As Chorus 1

Bridge

C#5 E5　B5　　　　A5 E B5　C#5
And for　how long I love____my lov - er,

C#5 E5　B5　　　　A5 E B5　C#5
For　how long I love____my lov - er. And now, now,

C#5 E5　B5　　　　　　A5 E B5　C#5
For　how long, long, I love____my lov - er, now, now,

C#5 E5　B5　　　　　A5 E B5　C#5
For　how long, long, I love____my lov - er, now, now.

(cont. in background)

C#m7 E5　B5　　　　　Asus2　E　Bsus4 C#m7
(For　how long, long, I love_____ my lov　-　er, now, now.)

C#m7　　　　　E5 Bsus4
And I feel loved.

　　Asus2　E　　Bsus4 C#m7　　　　　　　E5　Bsus4
I feel it all　　over now,　　now and I feel loved.

　　Asus2　E　　Bsus4 C#m7　　　　　　　E5　Bsus4
I feel it all　　over now,　　now and I feel loved.

　　Asus2　E　　Bsus4 C#m7　　　　　　　E5　Bsus4
I feel it all　　over now,　　now and I feel loved.

　　Asus2　E　　Bsus4 C#m7　　　　　　　E5　Bsus4
I feel it all　　over now,　　now and I feel loved.

　　Asus2　E　　Bsus4 C#m7
I feel it all　　over now,　　now and I feel loved.

Outro

C#5 E5　B5　　　　A5　E　B5　C#5
For　how long I love____ my lov - er now, now,

C#5 E5　B5　　　　A5　B5 C#5
For　how long I love____ my lover.

I See Fire

Words & Music by Ed Sheeran

Am   Fmaj7   G   C   Dsus2   Dm

To match original recording, tune ukulele up one semitone

Intro

N.C.
Oh, misty eye of the mountain below,

Keep careful watch of my brothers' souls.

And should the sky be filled with fire and smoke,

                  Am
Keep watching over Durin's sons.

Link 1 | Am Fmaj7 | G Am | Am Fmaj7 | G Am   ‖

Verse 1

Am   C   G   Fmaj7
If this is to end in fire, then we should all burn to - gether,

         Am   C   G   Dsus2
Watch the flames climb high into the night.

         Am   C   G   Fmaj7
Calling out father,   oh, stand by and we will

         Dm   C   Fmaj7
Watch the flames burn auburn on the mountain side high.

Link 2 | Am Fmaj7 | G Am   ‖

Verse 2

Am   C   G   Fmaj7
And if we should die to - night, then we should all die to - gether,

        Am   C   G   Dsus2
Raise a glass of wine for the last time.

        Am   C   G   Fmaj7
Calling out father,   oh, prepare as we will

          Dm   C   Fmaj7
Watch the flames burn auburn on the mountain side,

        Dm   C   Fmaj7
Deso - lation comes upon the sky.

Chorus 1

(Fmaj7)   Am Fmaj7 G   Am
Now, I see fire   inside the mountain,

       Fmaj7 G   Am
I see fire   burning the trees.

         Fmaj7 G   Am
And I see fire_____ hollowing souls,

        Fmaj7 G   Dsus2
I see fire,_____ blood in the breeze.

And I hope that you remember me.

Link 3 | Am Fmaj7 | G Am | Am Fmaj7 | G Am   ‖

Verse 3

Am   C   G   Fmaj7
Oh, should my people fall, then surely I'll do the same,

          Am   C   G   Dsus2
Confined in mountain halls, we got too close to the flame.

        Am   C   G   Fmaj7
Calling out father,   oh, hold fast and we will

          Dm   C   Fmaj7
Watch the flames burn auburn on the mountain side,

        Dm   C   Fmaj7
Deso - lation comes upon the sky.

Chorus 2   As Chorus 1

Bridge

Dsus2　　Dm　　Am　　　　　　C　　　　G
And if the night is burning, I will cover my eyes,

　　　　　　　Dm　　Am　　　　　C　　　　G
For if the dark re - turns, then my brothers will die.

　　　　　　　　Dm　　　　　Am　　　　　　　　C　　　　　　　G
And as the sky is falling down it crashed in - to this lonely town,

　　　　　　　　　　Dm
And with that shadow upon the ground

　　C　　　　Fmaj7　　　　　　　　　G
I hear my people screaming out.__

Chorus 3

(G)　　　　　Am　Fmaj7　G　　　　Am
Now, I see fire　　　　　inside the mountain,

　　　　　　Fmaj7　G　　　　　Am
I see fire　　　　burning the trees.

　　　　　　　　Fmaj7　G　　　　Am
And I see fire_____ hollowing souls,

　　　　　　Fmaj7　G　　　　Am
I see fire,_____ blood in the breeze.

Outro

Am　　　　　Fmaj7　　　　　　　　　　　G　　　Am
I see fire, oh　　you know I saw a city burning.

　　　　　　　　Fmaj7　　　　　　　　　G　　　Am
And I see fire, feel the heat upon my skin, yeah.

　　　　　　　　Fmaj7　　G　Am
And I see fire, ooh._____

　　　　　　　　Fmaj7　　　　　G　　　Am
And I see fire burn auburn on the mountain side.

Kiss Me

Words & Music by Ed Sheeran, Julie Frost & Justin Franks

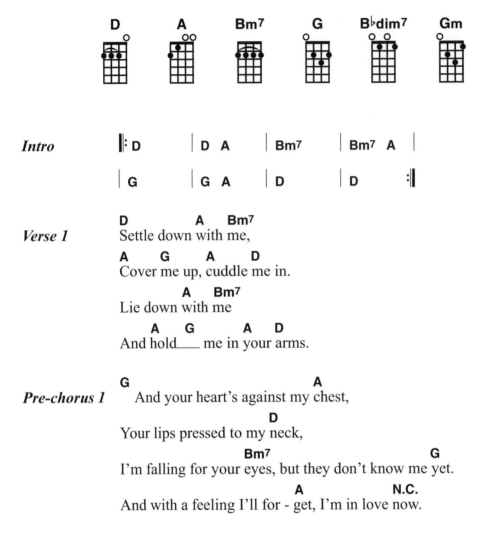

Intro

‖: D | D A | Bm⁷ | Bm⁷ A |

| G | G A | D | D :‖

Verse 1

D   A   Bm⁷
Settle down with me,

A   G   A   D
Cover me up, cuddle me in.

       A   Bm⁷
Lie down with me

   A   G   A D
And hold____ me in your arms.

Pre-chorus 1

    G   A
And your heart's against my chest,

                 D
Your lips pressed to my neck,

               Bm⁷
I'm falling for your eyes, but they don't know me yet.   G

                   A   N.C.
And with a feeling I'll for - get, I'm in love now.

Chorus 1

D   A   Bm7
Kiss me like you wanna be loved,

     A   G   A   D
You wanna be loved, you wanna be loved.

           A   Bm7
This feels like falling in love,

A   G   A   D
Falling in love, we're falling in love.

Verse 2

D   A   Bm7
Settle down with me

             A   G   A   D
And I'll be your safe - ty, you'll be my la - dy.

         A Bm7
I was made   to keep your body warm,

A   G   A   D
   But I'm cold as the wind blows   so hold me in your arms.

Pre-chorus 2   As Pre-chorus 1

Chorus 2   As Chorus 1

Instrumental

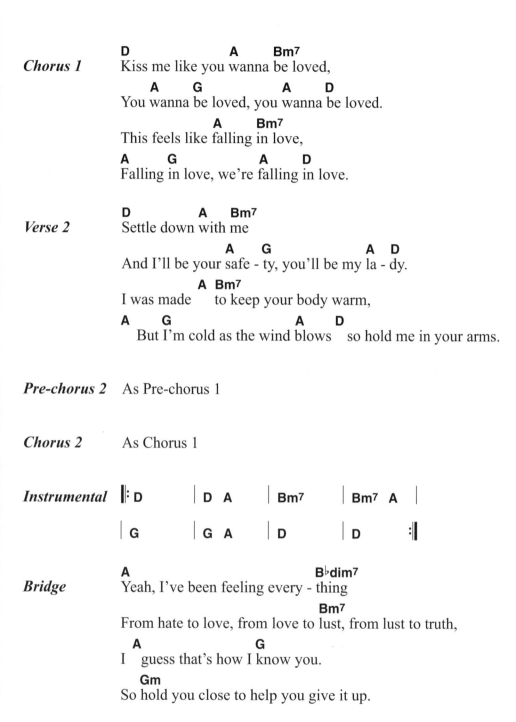

‖: D | D   A | Bm7 | Bm7   A |

| G | G   A | D | D   :‖

Bridge

A   B♭dim7
Yeah, I've been feeling every - thing

                           Bm7
From hate to love, from love to lust, from lust to truth,

   A   G
I   guess that's how I know you.

     Gm
So hold you close to help you give it up.

Chorus 3

    D   A   Bm7
    So kiss me like you wanna be loved,

     A   G   A   D
You wanna be loved, you wanna be loved.

          A   Bm7
This feels like falling in love,

A   G   A   D
Falling in love, we're falling in love.

Chorus 4   As Chorus 1

Outro   ‖: D | D A | Bm7 | Bm7 A |

              | G | G A | D | D   :‖ *Fade out*

Lego House

Words & Music by Ed Sheeran, Christopher Leonard & Jake Gosling

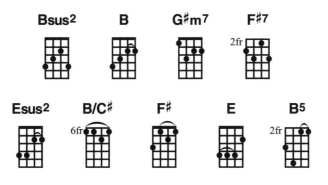

Intro

| Bsus2 | Bsus2 B | G#m7 | G#m7 F#7 ‖

Verse 1

Bsus2   B   G#m7   F#7   Bsus2
I'm gonna pick up the   pieces and build a Le - go   house,

            B   G#m7   F#7 B
If things go wrong we can knock it down.

                    B G#m7   F#7   B
My three words have two   meanings, there's one thing on my mind,

           B G#m7   F#7
It's all for_____ you.

Bridge 1

        B
   And it's dark in the cold December,

                   B   G#m7
But I've got you to keep me warm.

F#7 B
      If you're broken I will mend you

              B
And I'll keep you sheltered from the

G#m7   N.C.   Esus2
   Storm that's rag - ing on_____ now.

Chorus 1

  B   B/C♯   G♯m7
   I'm out of touch, I'm out of love,

           B F♯
I'll pick you up when you're getting down.

      B   E
And out of all these things I've done,

      F♯   B
I think I love you better now.

        B/C♯   G♯m7
I'm out of sight, I'm out of mind,

       B/C♯ F♯
I'll do it all for you in time.

       B   E
And out of all these things I've done,

      F♯   B
I think I love you better now.

   G♯m7 Esus2
Now.

Verse 2

 Bsus2   B G♯m7   Esus2 Bsus2
  I'm gonna paint you by numbers and colour you in,

      B   G♯m7   Esus2 Bsus2
If things go right we can frame it and put you on a wall.

        B G♯m7   Esus2 Bsus2
And it's so hard to say it, but I've been here be - fore,

        B G♯m7   Esus2
Now I'll surrender up my heart and swap it for yours.

Chorus 2

  B   B/C♯   G♯m7
   I'm out of touch, I'm out of love,

           B F♯
I'll pick you up when you're getting down.

      B   E
And out of all these things I've done,

      F♯   B
I think I love you better now.

        B/C♯   G♯m7
I'm out of sight, I'm out of mind,

       B F♯
I'll do it all for you in time.

       B   E
And out of all these things I've done,

      F♯
I think I love you better now.

Middle

<pre>
G♯m7   F♯   E
    Don't hold me down,___
            F♯
I think the braces are breaking
        E   F♯
And it's more than I can take.___
</pre>

Bridge 2

<pre>
B
    And it's dark in the cold December,
                    B   G♯m7
But I've got you to keep me warm.
F♯7 B
        If you're broken I will mend you

And I'll keep you sheltered from the
G♯m7   F♯7
    Storm that's raging on now.
</pre>

Chorus 3   As Chorus 2

Chorus 4

<pre>
B5   B/C♯   G♯m7
    I'm out of touch, I'm out of love,
                            B5   B
I'll pick you up when you're getting down.
                    G♯m7   Esus2
And out of all these things I've done,
                    B   B5
I will love you better now.
</pre>

Little Bird

Words & Music by Ed Sheeran

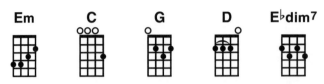

Em   C   G   D   E♭dim7

To match original recording, tune ukulele up one semitone

Intro | Em | C | G | G   D ||

Verse 1

Em   C
If we take this bird in   with its broken leg,
G   D
We could nurse it, she said.
Em   C
Come inside for a little lie down with me,
G   D
If you fall asleep it wouldn't be the worst thing.
               C   G
But when I wake up your make-up is on my shoulder,
D   C
And tell me, if I lie down would you stay now
                 D
And let me hold you? Oh.

Chorus 1

E♭dim7   Em   C
But if I kiss you will your mouth read this truth?
                   G
Darling, how I miss you, strawberries taste how lips do.
D   Em   C
And it's not com - plete yet, mustn't get our feet wet,
                   G
'Cause that leads to regret, diving in too soon.
D   C   D   Em
And I'll owe it all to you, oh,   my little bird,
C   G   D
My little bird.

Verse 2

Em   **C**
  If we take a walk out   in the morning dew,

G   **D**
  We could lay down so I'm next to you.

Em   **C**
  And come inside for a little home-made tea,

G   **D**
  And if you fall asleep, then at least you're next to me.

      C   **G**
And if I wake up you see, it's late, love, go back to sleep

D   **C**
  I'm covered by nature and I'm safe now

        D
Underneath this oak tree with you beside me.

Chorus 2

E♭dim7   **Em**   **C**
  But if I kiss you will your mouth read this truth?

       G
Darling, how I miss you, strawberries taste how lips do.

D   **Em**   **C**
  And it's not com - plete yet, mustn't get our feet wet,

       G
'Cause that leads to regret, diving in too soon.

D   **C**   **D**   **C**
  And I'll owe it all to you, oh,   my little bird,

D   **Em**   **G**
  My little bird,

     C
My little bird,

D   **Em**   **G**
  My little bird.

Bridge

G   **C**   **D**
And of all these things I'm sure of,

  C   **D**
I'm not quite certain of your love.

     C   **D**
And you made me scream, but then I made you cry

     C   **D**
When I left that little bird with its broken leg to die.

Chorus 3

D   Em   C

But if I kiss you will your mouth read this truth?

                     G

Darling, how I miss you, strawberries taste how lips do.

D   Em   C

   And it's not com - plete yet, mustn't get our feet wet,

                     G

'Cause that leads to regret, diving in too soon.

D   C   D   Em C

   But I'll owe it all to you, oh,   my little bird

            G   D

My little bird, whoa, oh, oh.

          Em   C

My little bird,

          G

My little bird,

D   C

You're my little bird.

One

Words & Music by Ed Sheeran

| D | A | Bm | G | E5 | Dmaj7 | D5 |

Intro | D   ‖

Verse 1
D   A   Bm
Tell me that you'd turn down the man who asks for your hand
                  G   D
'Cause you're waiting for me.

And I know, you're gonna be away a while,
          A Bm   G D
But I've got no plans at all to leave.
          A   G
Would you take away my hopes and dreams
          E5   G   A
And just stay with me? Ooh.

Chorus 1
D
All my senses come to life
          Dmaj7
While I'm stumbling home as drunk as I
    Bm   G   A
Have ever been and I'll never leave a - gain,
        G   A
'Cause you are the only one.
          D
And all my friends have gone to find
          Dmaj7
Another place to let their hearts collide.
      Bm   G   A
Just promise me, you'll never leave a - gain, now,
        G   A   D
'Cause you are the only one.

Verse 2

D   A
Take my hand and my heart and soul, I will
Bm   **G**   **D**
  Only have these eyes for you.

And you know, everything changes but
                     A **Bm**   **G**   **D**
We'll be strang - ers if we see this through.
       A   **G**
We could stay within these walls and bleed
     E⁵   **G** **A**
Or just stay with me, oh Lord, now

Chorus 2

D
All my senses come to life
          Dmaj⁷
While I'm stumbling home as drunk as I
    Bm   **G**   **A**
Have ever been and I'll never leave a - gain, now,
    G   **A**
'Cause you are the only one.
     D
And all my friends have gone to find
    Dmaj⁷
Another place to let their hearts collide.
    Bm   **A**
Just promise me, you'll always be a friend, now,
    G   **A**
'Cause you are the only one.

Bridge

G   **D⁵**   **A**
  Stumbling half drunk, getting myself lost,
           G   **Bm** **G**
I am so gone, so tell me the way home.
     D⁵   **G**   **A**
I listen to sad songs, singing a - bout love
       (Bm)
And where it goes wrong.

| **Bm** **G** | **D⁵** | **Bm** **G** | **D⁵** | |
(wrong)_____

| **Bm** **G** | **D⁵** | **Bm** **A** | **G** | **G** | ‖
_____ ooh._____

56

Chorus 3

D
All my senses come to life

      Dmaj⁷
While I'm stumbling home as drunk as I

  Bm   **G**   **A**
Have ever been and I'll never leave a - gain,

    G   **A**
'Cause you are the only one.

   D
And all my friends have gone to find

      Dmaj⁷
Another place to let their hearts collide.

  Bm   **A**
Just promise me, you'll always be a friend,

    G   **A**   **D5**
'Cause you are the only one.

The Man

Words & Music by Ed Sheeran

A   Bm   F♯m   G

Intro   A | Bm   F♯m | G   A | Bm   F♯m | G   A ‖

Verse 1

(A)   Bm
Now I don't wanna hate you, just wish you'd never gone for the man
F♯m G   A   Bm
      And waited two weeks at least before you let him take you.
                                                     F♯m
I stayed true, I kind of knew you liked the dude from private school,
      G   A   Bm
He's waiting for the time to move, I knew he had his eyes on you.
                                                  F♯m
He's not the right guy for you, don't hate me cause I write the truth,
      G   A Bm
No, I would never lie to you, but it was never fine to lose you.
                                        F♯m
And what a way to find out, it never came from my mouth,
                                                  A   Bm
You never changed your mind, but you were just a - fraid to mind out.
                                       F♯m
But fuck it, I won't be changing the subject I love it,
G
 I'll make your little secret public, it's nothing.
A   Bm   F♯m
   I'm just disgusted with the skeletons you sleep with in your closet
      G
To get back at me.

Trapped and I'm lacking sleep,
      A   Bm   F♯m
The fact is you're mad at me because I backtrack so casually.

cont.

              G
You're practically my family,
                           A   Bm
If we married then I'll guess you'd have to be.
                                         F♯m
But tragically our love just lost the will to live,
              G
But would I kill to give it one more shot, I think not.

Chorus 1

A Bm   F♯m   G
I don't love you baby, I don't need you baby,
A Bm   F♯m   G
I don't want you, no, anymore.___
A Bm   F♯m   G
I don't love you baby, I don't need you baby,
A Bm   F♯m   G
I don't wanna love you, no, anymore.___

Verse 2

(G)   A   Bm
Recently I tend to zone out up in my headphones to "Holocene",
     F♯m   G
You promised your body but I'm away so much
                 A   Bm
I stay more celi - bate than in a monastery.
                     F♯m
I'm not cut out for life on the road
          G
'Cause I didn't know I'd miss you this much
         A   Bm
And at the time we'd just go, so sue me,
              F♯m
I guess I'm not the man that you need,
     G   A   Bm
Ever since you went to uni, I've been sofa surfing with a rucksack,
                                     F♯m
Full of less cash and I guess that could get bad.
          G
But when I broke the industry, that's when I broke your heart,
A Bm   F♯m
  I was supposed to chart and celebrate, but good things are over fast.
G
I know it's hard to deal with and see this,
          A   Bm
I tend to turn you off and switch on my professional features.

cont.

    F♯m   **G**
Then I turn the music off

                A   **Bm**
And all I'm left with is to pick up my per - sonal pieces.

           F♯m
Jesus, I never really want to be - lieve this,

   G
Got ad - vice from my dad

         A **Bm**
And he told me that family is all I'll ever have and need,

       F♯m   **G**
I guess I'm unaware of it: suc - cess is nothing

If you have no one there left to share it with.

Chorus 2   As Chorus 1

       (G)   **A** **Bm**
Verse 3   And since you left, I've given up my days off,

            F♯m
It's what I need to stay strong,

   G   **A** **Bm**
I know you have a day job but mine is twenty four se - ven.

I feel like writing a book, I guess I lied in the hook,
F♯m
  'Cause I still love you and I need you by my side if I could.
A Bm
  The irony is if my career and music didn't exist,
F♯m   **G**
  In six years, yeah, you'd probably be my wife with a kid.
A Bm
  I'm frightened to think if I depend on cider and drink,
F♯m   **G**
  And lighting a spliff, I fall into a spiral and it's
A Bm
  Just hiding my misguiding thoughts that I'm trying to kill,
F♯m   **G**
  And I'd be writing my will before I'm twenty seven,
A **Bm**   **F♯m**
I'll die from a thrill, go down in history as just a wasted talent
    G   **A**   **Bm**
Can I face the challenge, or did I make a mistake e - rasing?

cont.

                                                    F♯m
It's only therapy, my thoughts just get a - head of me,

      G   **A**   **Bm**
E - ventually I'll be fine I know that it was never meant to be.

                                  F♯m   **G**
Either way I guess I'm not prepared, but I'll say this,

                            A   **Bm**
These things happen for a reason and you can't change.

                       F♯m
Take my apology, I'm sorry for the honesty,

      G
But I had to get this off my chest.

Chorus 3   As Chorus 1

Outro   **A** ‖: **Bm** **F♯m** │ **G**   **A** │ **Bm** **F♯m** │ **G**   **A** :‖

                                      Repeat to fade

Nina

Words & Music by Ed Sheeran, Johnny McDaid,
Jermaine Scott, Jay Hippolyte & Isra Lohata

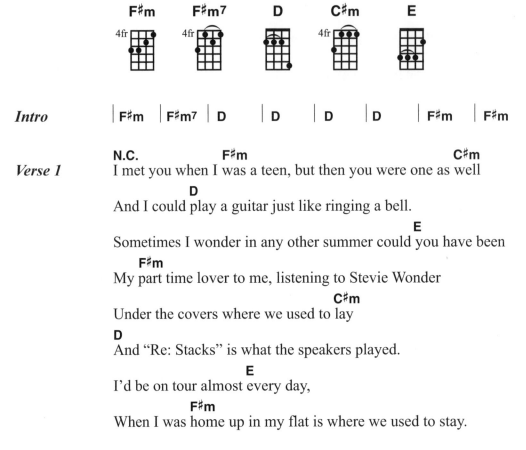

Intro　| F♯m | F♯m7 | D　| D　| D　| D　| F♯m | F♯m ‖

Verse 1

N.C.　　　　　　　　F♯m　　　　　　　　　　　　　　　　　C♯m
I met you when I was a teen, but then you were one as well

　　　　　D
And I could play a guitar just like ringing a bell.

　　　　　　　　　　　　　　　　　　　　　　　　　E
Sometimes I wonder in any other summer could you have been

　　F♯m
My part time lover to me, listening to Stevie Wonder

　　　　　　　　　　　　　　　C♯m
Under the covers where we used to lay

D
And "Re: Stacks" is what the speakers played.

　　　　　　　　　　　E
I'd be on tour almost every day,

　　　　　F♯m
When I was home up in my flat is where we used to stay.

Verse 2

F♯m　　　　　　　　　　　　　　　C♯m
Just watching the DVD, smoking illegal weed,

D
　Getting high as two kites when we needed to breathe.

　　　　　　　　　　E
We'd use each other's air just for the people to see,

F♯m
　And stay up all night like when we needed to sleep.

cont.   We'd go anywhere, our minds would take us,

C♯m   D
    And I'd say you were beautiful without your make-up.

                                                    E
And you don't even need to worry about your weight 'cause

F♯m
We can all be loved the way that God made us.

And time's the only reason that we could break up,

C♯m   D
    'Cause you would always tell me I'm away too much.

                            E   **F♯m**
Distance is relative to the time that it takes to get on a plane

Or make a mistake, so say it again.

F♯m   **D**
Chorus 1   Oh Nina, you should go, Nina,

'Cause I ain't ever coming home, Nina
E   **F♯m**
Oh, won't you leave me now.

And I've been living on the road, Nina,
                            D
But then again you should know, Nina,

'Cause that's you and me both, Nina,
E   **F♯m**
Oh, won't you leave me now, now

F♯m
Verse 3   And every weekend in the winter you'd be wearing my hoodie
        C♯m D
With draw-strings pulled tight to keep your face from the cold.
                                            E
Taking day trips to the local where we'd eat on our own,
                    F♯m
'Cause every day when I was away we'd only speak on the phone.

cont.   Watching "Blue Planet" creating new habits,

C#m   **D**

Acting as if we were two rabbits,

And then you'd vanish back to the burrow with all the Celtics.

E

I disappear, you call me selfish, I understand, but I can't help it.

I put my job over everything, except my family and friends,

   C#m   **D**

But you'll be in between forever

So I guess we'll have to take a step back,

         E   **F#m**

Overlook the situ - ation, 'cause mixing business and feelings

Will only lead to complications.

And I'm not saying we should be taking a break,

      C#m   **D**

Just re - e - valuate, quit before we make a mistake and it's too late.

                          E   **F#m**

So we can either deal with the pain or wait to get on a plane,

But in a day we'd have to say it again.

Chorus 2   As Chorus 1

               N.C. (F#m)

Bridge   Love will come and love will go, but you can make it on your own.

Sing that song, go, oh won't you leave me now.

People grow and fall apart, but you can mend your broken heart,

Take it back, go, oh won't you leave me now.

(w/bridge lyrics in background)

Chorus 3

F♯m **D**
Oh Nina, you should go, Nina,

'Cause I ain't ever coming home, Nina
E **F♯m**
Oh, won't you leave me now.

And I've been living on the road, Nina,
  D
But then again you should know, Nina,

'Cause that's you and me both, Nina,
E **F♯m**
Oh, won't you leave me now, now.

Chorus 4 As Chorus 3

Outro

F♯m	F♯m7	D	D	
D	D	F♯m	F♯m	‖

Runaway

Words & Music by Ed Sheeran & Pharrell Williams

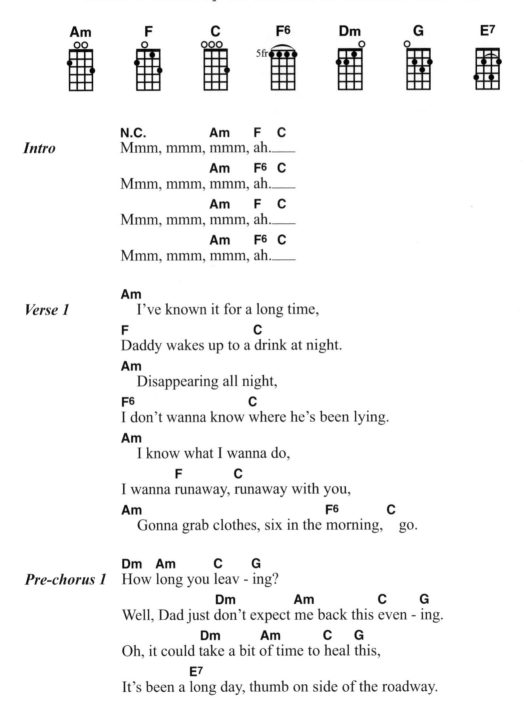

Intro

|N.C.|Am|F|C|
|Mmm, mmm, mmm, ah.____|

|Am|F6|C|
|Mmm, mmm, mmm, ah.____|

|Am|F|C|
|Mmm, mmm, mmm, ah.____|

|Am|F6|C|
|Mmm, mmm, mmm, ah.____|

Verse 1

Am
 I've known it for a long time,
F   **C**
Daddy wakes up to a drink at night.
Am
  Disappearing all night,
F6   **C**
I don't wanna know where he's been lying.
Am
  I know what I wanna do,
          F   **C**
I wanna runaway, runaway with you,
Am   **F6**   **C**
  Gonna grab clothes, six in the morning,   go.

Pre-chorus 1

Dm Am   **C   G**
How long you leav - ing?
              Dm   **Am**   **C   G**
Well, Dad just don't expect me back this even - ing.
              Dm   **Am**   **C   G**
Oh, it could take a bit of time to heal this,
              E7
It's been a long day, thumb on side of the roadway.

Chorus 1

N.C.   Am   F C
But I love him from the skin to my bones,
                     Am   F6 C
But I don't wanna live in his home.
                     Am   F C
There's nothing to say 'cause he knows
                        Am   F6 C
I'll just run a - way and be on my own.

Verse 2

Am
  I've never seen my dad cry,
F   C
Cold as stone in the kitchen light.
Am
  I tell you it's about time,
   F6   C
But I was raised to keep quiet.
Am
  And this is what I'm gonna do,
    F   C
Gonna runaway, gonna make that move,
Am   F6   C
  Gonna grab clothes and when it's morning, go.

Pre-chorus 2   As Pre-chorus 1

Chorus 2   As Chorus 1

Verse 3

(Am)   (F)
  Backpack and a flat cap turned to the back
          (C)
As I packed my clothes up,
(Am)   (F)   (C)
  My dad wasn't down with that plan to attack, intends to show love.
Am   F   C
  I don't wanna live this way, gonna take my things and go,
Am   F   C
  If things change in a matter of days, I could be persuaded to hold on.

Pre-chorus 3

Dm   Am   C

Our Mama was the same, but none of us are saints,

                G   Dm   Am

I guess that God knows that   I don't wanna runaway

                     C   G

But one of these days I might just show that.

Dm   Am   C   G

Put my home in a suitcase, tie both shoelaces, and hope that

E7

Things change, but for now I leave town

With a backpack on my shoulder.

Chorus 3

N.C.   Am   F C

I love him from the skin to my bones,

                   Am   F6 C

But I don't wanna live in his home.

                   Am   F C

There's nothing to say 'cause he knows

               Am   N.C.

I'll just run a - way and be on my own. Oh, mmm.

Photograph

Words & Music by Ed Sheeran & Johnny McDaid

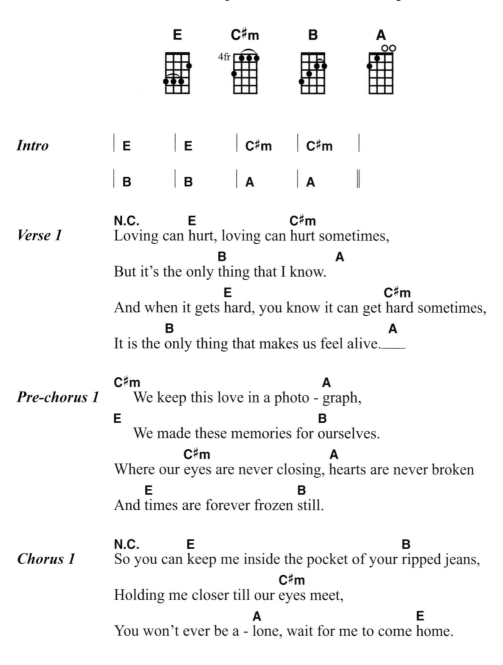

Intro

| E | E | C#m | C#m |

| B | B | A | A |

Verse 1

       N.C.   E   C#m
Loving can hurt, loving can hurt sometimes,

                 B   A
But it's the only thing that I know.

                      E   C#m
And when it gets hard, you know it can get hard sometimes,

                 B   A
It is the only thing that makes us feel alive.___

Pre-chorus 1

       C#m   A
    We keep this love in a photo - graph,

 E
    We made these memories for ourselves.   B

             C#m   A
Where our eyes are never closing, hearts are never broken

          E   B
And times are forever frozen still.

Chorus 1

       N.C.   E   B
So you can keep me inside the pocket of your ripped jeans,

                        C#m
Holding me closer till our eyes meet,

                   A   E
You won't ever be a - lone, wait for me to come home.

Verse 2

N.C.   E   C♯m
Loving can heal, loving can mend your soul
          B   A
And it's the only thing that I know, know.
                        E   C♯m
I swear it will get easier, remember that with every piece of you,
          B   A
And it's the only thing we take with us when we die.

Pre-chorus 2 As Pre-chorus 1

Chorus 2

N.C.   E   B
So you can keep me inside the pocket of your ripped jeans,
                              C♯m
Holding me closer till our eyes meet,
                          A
You won't ever be a - lone.
                      E   B
And if you hurt me, that's okay baby, only words bleed.
                             C♯m
Inside these pages you just hold me
                          A   C♯m
And I won't ever let you go, wait for me to come home,
                          A
Wait for me to come home,
                          E
Wait for me to come home,
                          B
Wait for me to come home, ooh.

Chorus 3

(B)   E   B
You can fit me inside the necklace you got when you were sixteen,
                             C♯m
Next to your heartbeat where I should be,
                          A
Keep it deep within your soul.
                      E   B
And if you hurt me, well, that's okay baby, only words bleed,
                             C♯m
Inside these pages you just hold me
                          A
And I won't ever let you go.

70

Chorus 4
        (A)   **E**   **B**
And when I'm a - way, I will remember how you kissed me

                               C♯m
Under the lamp post back on Sixth Street,

                                   A   **N.C.**
Hearing you whisper through the phone,   "Wait for me to come home."

The Parting Glass

Words & Music by Ed Sheeran, Jake Gosling & Peter Gosling

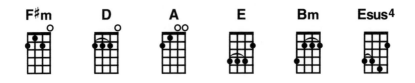

Verse 1

F#m   D   A   E
Of all the money   that e'er I had,

F#m   D   A   E
I've spent it in___ good company.

F#m   D   A   E
And all the harm___ that e'er I've done,

F#m D A   D   E F#m
A - las   it was to none but me.

A   D   A   D
And all I've done for want of wit,

Bm   A   D   Esus4   E
To memo - ry   now I can't re - call.

F#m D   A   E
So fill to me the parting glass,

F#m D A A   D   E F#m
Good night and joy be   with you all.

Verse 2

F#m   D   A   E
Of all the comrades that e'er I had,

F#m D   A   E
They are sorry for my going a - way.

F#m D   A   E
And all the sweethearts that e'er I had,

F#m   A   D E F#m
They would wish me one more day to stay.

A   D   A   D
But since it falls un - to my lot,

Bm   A   D   E
That I should rise and you should not.

F#m D   A   E
I'll gently rise and I'll softly call,

F#m D A A   D   E F#m
Good night and joy be   with you all.

Verse 3

F♯m   D   A   E
A man may drink and not be drunk,

F♯m   D   A   E
A man may fight and not be slain.

F♯m   D   A   E
A man may court a pretty girl,

F♯m D A   A   D   E F♯m
And per - haps be wel - comed back a - gain.

A   D   A   D
But since it has so ought to be,

Bm   A   D   Esus4 E
By a time to rise and a time to fall.

F♯m D   A   E
Come fill to me the parting glass,

F♯m D A A   D   E F♯m
Good night and joy be   with you all.

F♯m D A A   D   E F♯m
Good night and joy be   with you all.

Shirtsleeves

Words & Music by Ed Sheeran

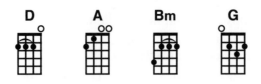

Verse 1

```
      N.C.           D
      I can taste salt water
                     A           Bm
      And if I blink a - gain we'll be sinking in,
                                 G           D
      So we'll learn to swim in the oceans you made.
                     A               Bm
      I'll hold you and you'll think of him
                                 G
      And pretty soon you'll be floating away.
```

Pre-chorus 1

```
      G                       A
          And I'll hold on to the words you spoke of,
      D               Bm
          Anchored down in your throat, love.
      G                       A
          And I'm captain of the sinking boat now
      G
          With just one armband to carry me home.
```

Chorus 1

```
      D
          When salted tears won't dry,
      A   Bm        G           A   D
      I'll wipe my shirt - sleeve under your eyes.

      These hearts will be flooded tonight,
      A   Bm        G           A   D
      I'll wipe my shirt - sleeve under your eyes.
                                     A   D
      Your eyes, your eyes, your eyes, your eyes, your eyes.
```

Verse 2

N.C.   D
I still taste salt water

        A   Bm
On my lips from your kiss, bitterness,

                G   D
And I'll drown within the oceans you made.

            A   Bm
And I hate to love you, these cuts are covered in your make-up,

        G
I'll never trust you again, you can just be a friend.

Pre-chorus 2   As Pre-chorus 1

Chorus 2

D
  When salted tears won't dry,

A Bm   G   A   D
I'll wipe my shirt - sleeve under your eyes

These hearts will be flooded tonight,

A Bm   G   A   D
I'll wipe my shirt - sleeve under your eyes.

Bridge

G   A
Your eyes, your lips, your mouth your thighs, your back,

Bm   D   G
  You drive me wild to - night, the fact is I,___

        A   Bm
I'm on the way home, I'm on the way home.

D   G
  I lied, I tried to cry but I'm,

    A   (D)
I'm drowning in the oceans you made.___

Instrumental ‖: D | Bm | G | A :‖

Chorus 3

D
    When salted tears won't dry,
A Bm   G   A   D
I'll wipe my shirt - sleeve under your eyes.

These hearts will be flooded tonight,
A Bm   G   A   D
I'll wipe my shirt - sleeve under your eyes.
                                          A   D   (G)
Your eyes, your eyes, your eyes, your eyes, your eyes.

Sing

Words & Music by Ed Sheeran & Pharrell Williams

| *Intro* | | Am | | Am | | Am | | Am | ‖ |

Verse 1

    N.C.   **Am**
It's late in the evening, glass on the side,

I've been sat with you for most of the night,
      Dm
Ignoring everybody here we wish they would disappear

So maybe we could get down now.
Am
I don't wanna know if you're getting ahead of the program,
            Dm
I want you to be mine, lady, and to hold your body close.

Take another step into the no-man's land

For the longest time, lady.

Pre-chorus 1
    Am
I need you darling, come on set the tone,

If you feel you're falling, won't you let me know?
    Dm
Oh, oh-oh-oh, ooh-ooh, oh, oh-oh-oh, ooh-ooh.
Am
If you love me come on get involved,

Feel it rushing through you from your head to toe.
    Dm
Oh, oh-oh-oh, ooh-ooh, oh, oh-oh-oh, ooh-ooh. Sing!

	Am
Pre-chorus 1	Oh, oh, oh, oh-oh, oh, oh, oh, oh, oh, oh, oh-oh.

Oh, oh, oh, oh-oh, oh, oh, oh, oh, oh, oh, oh-oh. Louder!

Dm
Oh, oh, oh, oh-oh, oh, oh, oh, oh, oh, oh, oh-oh. Sing!

Oh, oh, oh, oh-oh, oh, oh, oh, oh, oh, oh, oh-oh.

	N.C. Am
Rap	This love is a - blaze, I saw flames from the side of the stage

And the fire brigade comes in a couple of days.

Until then we got nothing to say and nothing to know,

But something to drink and maybe something to smoke.
Dm
 Let it go until our roads are changed,

Singing "We Found Love" in a local rave, no,

I don't really know what I'm supposed to say

But I can just figure it out and hope and pray.
 Am
I told her my name and said, "It's nice to meet ya."

Then she handed me a bottle of water filled with tequila.

I already know she's a keeper,

Just from this one small act of kindness
       Dm
I'm in deep, deep. If anybody finds out,

I'm meant to drive home but I've drunk all of it now.

Not sobering up we just sit on the couch,

One thing led to another, now she's kissing my mouth.

Pre-chorus 2   As Pre-chorus 1

Chorus 2   As Chorus 1

                   Am
Bridge   Can you feel it?

                All the guys in here don't even wanna dance.

                Can you feel it?

                All that I can hear is music from the back.
                Dm
                Can you feel it?

                Found you hiding here so won't you take my hand darling

                Before the beat kicks in again?
                  Am
                Can you feel it? Ooh, ah, oh.
                Dm
                Can you feel it? Ooh, no, no, no, whoa, no, no.

                N.C.   **Am**
Chorus 3   Sing! I need you darling, come on set the tone,

                If you feel you're falling, won't you let me know?
                   Dm
                Oh, oh-oh-oh, ooh-ooh.

                Oh, oh-oh-oh, ooh-ooh. Sing!
                Am
                If you love me come on get involved,

                Feel it rushing through you from your head to toe.
                   Dm
                Oh, oh-oh-oh, ooh-ooh.

                Oh, oh-oh-oh, ooh-ooh. Sing!

Small Bump

Words & Music by Ed Sheeran

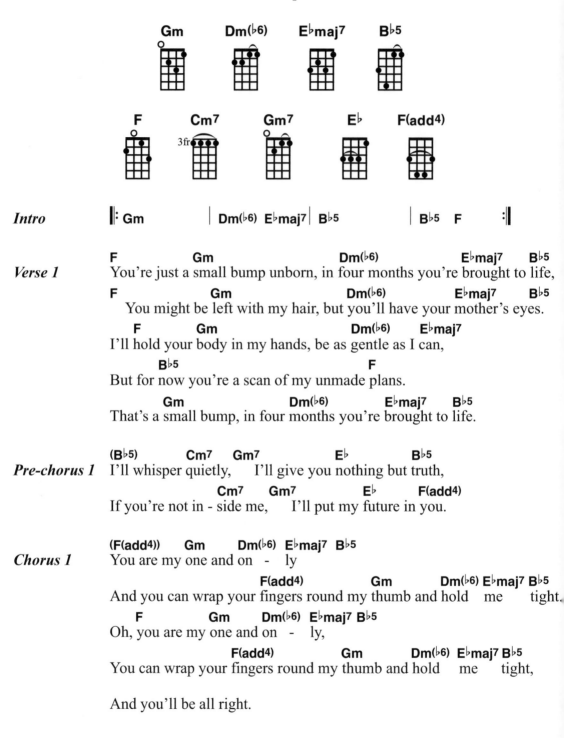

Intro

‖: Gm | Dm(♭6) E♭maj7 | B♭5 | B♭5 F :‖

Verse 1

F · · · · · Gm · · · · · · · Dm(♭6) · · · · · · · E♭maj7 · · B♭5
You're just a small bump unborn, in four months you're brought to life,

F · · · · · · · Gm · · · · · · · · · · Dm(♭6) · · · · · · · E♭maj7 · · B♭5
You might be left with my hair, but you'll have your mother's eyes.

· · F · · · · · · Gm · · · · · · · · · · Dm(♭6) · · · · · E♭maj7
I'll hold your body in my hands, be as gentle as I can,

· · · · B♭5 · F
But for now you're a scan of my unmade plans.

· · · · · Gm · · · · · · · · · Dm(♭6) · · · · · · E♭maj7 · · B♭5
That's a small bump, in four months you're brought to life.

Pre-chorus 1

(B♭5) · · · · Cm7 · Gm7 · · · · · · · E♭ · · · · · · · B♭5
I'll whisper quietly, · · I'll give you nothing but truth,

· · · · · · · · · · Cm7 · · Gm7 · · · · · · E♭ · · · · F(add4)
If you're not in - side me, · · I'll put my future in you.

Chorus 1

(F(add4)) · · · Gm · · · · Dm(♭6) E♭maj7 B♭5
You are my one and on · - · ly

· · · · · · · · · · · · · · F(add4) · · · · · · · · Gm · · · · · · · · Dm(♭6) E♭maj7 B♭5
And you can wrap your fingers round my thumb and hold · · me · · · · tight.

· · · · F · · · · · · · Gm · · · · · Dm(♭6) B♭5
Oh, you are my one and on · - · ly,

· · · · · · · · · · · · · · F(add4) · · · · · · · · Gm · · · · · · · · Dm(♭6) E♭maj7 B♭5
You can wrap your fingers round my thumb and hold · · me · · · · tight,

And you'll be all right.

Verse 2

N.C.   **Gm**   **Dm(♭6)**   **E♭maj7** **B♭5**
Ooh, you're just a small bump I know, you'll grow into   your skin.

       Gm   **Dm(♭6)**   **E♭maj7**   **B♭5**
With a smile like hers and a dimple be - neath your chin.

F   **Gm**   **Dm(♭6)**   **E♭maj7**
   Fingernails the size of a half grain of rice

   B♭5
And eyelids closed to be soon opened wide.

  Gm   **Dm(♭6)**   **E♭maj7**   **B♭5**
A small bump, in four months you'll   open your eyes.

Pre-chorus 2

(**B♭5**)   **Cm7**   **Gm7**   **E♭**   **B♭5**
And I'll hold you tightly,   I'll tell you nothing but truth,

       Cm7   **Gm7**   **E♭**   **F(add4)**
If you're not inside me,   I'll put my future in you.

Chorus 2   As Chorus 1

Bridge

F   **Cm7**   **Gm**
   Then you can lie with me with your tiny feet

      B♭5   **F**
When you're half asleep, I'll leave you be.

     Cm7   **Gm**
Right in front of me for a couple weeks

F   **E♭**   **(Fadd4)**
So I could keep you safe._____

Chorus 3

(**F(add4)**)   **Gm**   **Dm(♭6)** **E♭maj7** **B♭5**
'Cause you are my one and on - ly,

            F(add4)   **Gm**   **Dm(♭6)** **E♭maj7** **B♭5**
You can wrap your fingers round my thumb and hold   me   tight.

F   **Gm**   **Dm(♭6)** **E♭maj7** **B♭5**
You are my one and on - ly,

            F(add4)   **Gm**   **Dm(♭6)** **E♭maj7** **B♭5**
You can wrap your fingers round my thumb and hold   me   tight.

And you'll be all right.

Outro

B♭5   Gm   Dm(♭6)

'Cause you were just a small bump unborn for four months

E♭maj7 B♭5

Then torn from life.

Gm   Dm(♭6)   E♭maj7 B♭5

Maybe you were needed up there but we're still un - aware as why.

Thinking Out Loud

Words & Music by Ed Sheeran & Amy Wadge

D   D/F♯   G   A   Em   A7   Bm

Verse 1

D D/F♯   G   A
When your legs don't work like they used to before

D D/F♯   G   A
And I can't sweep you off of your feet.

D D/F♯   G   A
Will your mouth still remember the taste of my love?

D D/F♯   G   A
Will your eyes still smile from your cheeks?

Pre-chorus 1

(A)   D D/F♯   G A   D D/F♯ G A
And, darling, I   will be loving you   till we're seventy.__

      D D/F♯   G   A   D D/F♯
And, baby, my heart could still fall   as hard at twenty three.__

G   A   Em   A7   D
And I'm thinking 'bout how people fall in love in my - sterious ways,

Em   A7
Maybe just the touch of a hand.

    Em   A7   Bm
Well, me, I fall in love with you eve - ry single day

    Em   A7
And I just wanna tell you,__

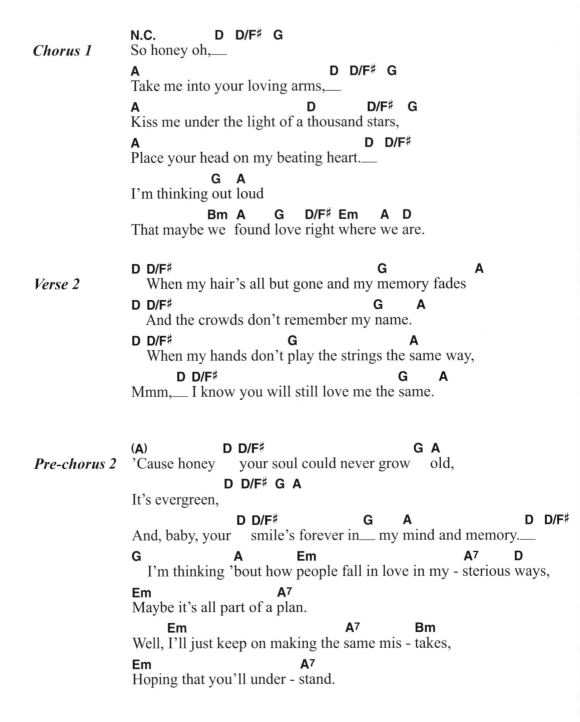

Chorus 1

N.C.   D D/F♯ G
So honey oh,__

A   D D/F♯ G
Take me into your loving arms,__

A   D   D/F♯ G
Kiss me under the light of a thousand stars,

A   D D/F♯
Place your head on my beating heart.__

          G A
I'm thinking out loud

        Bm A   G   D/F♯ Em   A D
That maybe we found love right where we are.

Verse 2

D D/F♯   G   A
    When my hair's all but gone and my memory fades

D D/F♯   G   A
    And the crowds don't remember my name.

D D/F♯   G   A
    When my hands don't play the strings the same way,

      D D/F♯   G   A
Mmm,__ I know you will still love me the same.

Pre-chorus 2

(A)   D D/F♯   G A
'Cause honey   your soul could never grow   old,

                 D D/F♯ G A
It's evergreen,

                D D/F♯   G   A   D D/F♯
And, baby, your   smile's forever in__ my mind and memory.__

G   A   Em   A7   D
   I'm thinking 'bout how people fall in love in my - sterious ways,

Em   A7
Maybe it's all part of a plan.

    Em   A7   Bm
Well, I'll just keep on making the same mis - takes,

Em   A7
Hoping that you'll under - stand.

Chorus 2

N.C.   D D/F♯ G
But, baby, now,___

A   D D/F♯ G
Take me into your loving arms,___

A   D   D/F♯ G
Kiss me under the light of a thousand stars,

A   D D/F♯
Place your head on my beating heart.___

           G A
Thinking out__ loud

          Bm A   G   D/F♯ Em   A D
That maybe we found love right where we are.

Instrumental   ‖: D D/F♯ | G A | D D/F♯ | G A   :‖

Chorus 3

(A)   D D/F♯ G
So, baby, now,___

A   D D/F♯ G
Take me into your loving arms,___

A   D   D/F♯
Kiss me under the light of a thousand stars,

      G   A   D D/F♯
Oh, darling, place your head on my beating heart.___

           G A
I'm thinking out__ loud

          Bm A   G   D/F♯ Em   A D
That maybe we found love right where we are.

          Bm A   G   D/F♯ Em   A D
Oh, baby, we found love right where we are.

        Bm A   G   D/F♯ Em   A D
And we found love right where we are.

Sunburn

Words & Music by Ed Sheeran

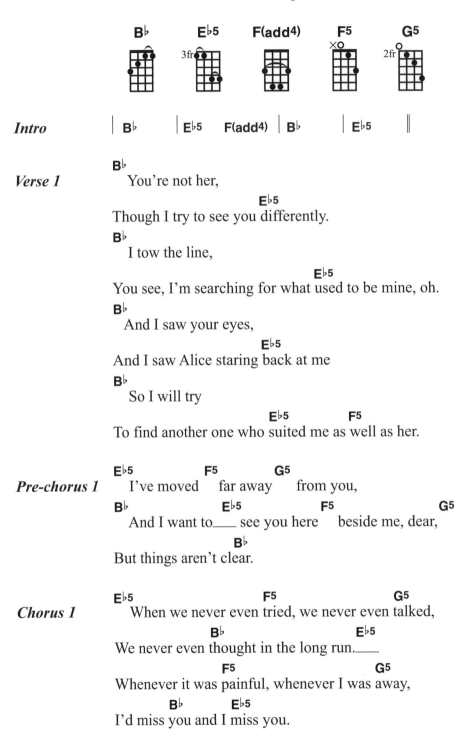

Intro | Bb | Eb5 F(add4) | Bb | Eb5 ‖

Verse 1

Bb
  You're not her,
                             Eb5
Though I try to see you differently.
Bb
  I tow the line,
                             Eb5
You see, I'm searching for what used to be mine, oh.
Bb
  And I saw your eyes,
                    Eb5
And I saw Alice staring back at me
Bb
  So I will try
                      Eb5   F5
To find another one who suited me as well as her.

Pre-chorus 1

Eb5   F5   G5
  I've moved   far away   from you,
Bb   Eb5   F5   G5
  And I want to___ see you here   beside me, dear,
                           Bb
But things aren't clear.

Chorus 1

Eb5   F5   G5
  When we never even tried, we never even talked,
                 Bb   Eb5
We never even thought in the long run.___
                F5   G5
Whenever it was painful, whenever I was away,
        Bb   Eb5
I'd miss you and I miss you.

Verse 2

B♭
　She was mine,
　　　　　　　　　　　E♭5
I was hers and all that's in between.
B♭
　If she would cry,
　　　　　　　　　E♭5
I would shelter her and keep her from the darkness that will be.

Pre-chorus 2
　　　　　　　　　F5　　　　G5
If I moved　　far away　　from you,
B♭　　　　　　E♭5　　　　　　F5　　　　　　　　G5
And I want to___ see you here　　beside me, dear,
　　　　　　　　　　B♭
But things aren't clear, woah.

Chorus 2　　　As Chorus 1

Bridge
　　　　　　B♭
　Don't drop me in, it's not my turn.
E♭5
　If you cut deep then I might learn
　　　　　　　G5　　　　　　F5　　　　　　B♭　　F(add4)　B♭
That you　　scarred and left me like sun - burn

Don't drop me in it's not my turn.
E♭5
　If you cut deep then I might learn
G5　　　　　　　　　F5　　　　　　　　E♭5
　That you scar and leave me like sun - burn

Chorus 3
E♭5　　　　　　　　　　　　　F5　　　　　　　　　G5
When we never even tried,　　we never even talked,
　　　　　　　B♭　　　　　　　　　E♭5
We never even thought in the long run.___
　　　　　F5　　　　　　　　G5
Whenever it was painful, whenever I was away,
　　　　B♭　　　E♭5
I'd miss you and I miss you.

Take It Back

Words & Music by Ed Sheeran & Johnny McDaid

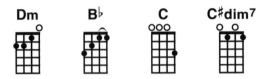

Dm   B♭   C   C♯dim7

Verse 1

Dm
I'm not a rapper; I'm a singer with a flow,

I've got a habit for spitting quicker lyrics, you know.
        B♭
You found me ripping the written out of the pages they sit in,
     C   **C♯dim7**
I never want to get bitten 'cause plagia - rism is hidden.
       Dm
Watch how I sit on the rhythm, prisoner with a vision,

Signed to a label, but didn't listen to any criticism.
       B♭
Thought you knew but you didn't, so perk your ears up and listen,
     C   **C♯dim7**
Studi - o is a system and you could say that I'm driven.
        Dm
And now it's   on to the next saga, we drink the best lager.

I'll never try to win you over like your stepfather.
B♭
   I do my own thing now, and get respect after,
C   **C♯dim7**
   And I'm avoiding the 'caine like it was "Get Carter".
Dm
   For four years I never had a place to stay,

But it's safe to say that it kept me grounded like a paperweight.
   B♭
At sixteen years old, yeah, I moved out of my home,
      C   **C♯dim7**
I was Macy Gray, I tried to say goodbye and I choked.

cont.

                    Dm
I went from sleeping at a subway station,

To sleeping with a movie star and adding to the population.
                   B♭
Not my imagi - nation, I don't wanna relax
                       C   **C♯dim7**
Would it hurt your repu - tation if I put it on wax?

I take it back now.

Chorus 1

Dm
Mmm, come on and take it back love,
B♭   **C**   **C♯dim7** **Dm**
  Come on and take it back for us.

Don't you fade into the back love,
B♭   **C**
   No.____

Verse 2

C♯dim7   **Dm**
  I take it back with the rhythm and blues,

With my rap pack I'll be singing the news.

Trying to act like Jack Black when I bring it to school,
B♭
  I make a beat with my feet by just hitting the loop.
C   **C♯dim7**
  Bringing the lyrics to prove that I can fit in these shoes,
Dm
  I give you the truth through the vocal booth.

And stars burst out on the scene like an Opal Fruit,
       B♭
They try to take aim like Beckham when he goes to shoot,
       C   **C♯dim7**
But then a - gain that's what they're sup - posed to do.
                    Dm
And I'm supposed to be calm, I tattooed the lyrics onto my arm,

Whispering: "Everything that happens is from now on."

B♭
I'll be ready to start again by the end of the song,

C
Still they're claiming that I handled it wrong.

C♯dim7   **Dm**
But then I've never had an enemy, except for the N.M.E.,

But I'll be selling twice as many copies as the magazines will ever be.
B♭   **C**
With only spectacles ahead of me and festival fees

C♯dim7
Are healthier than a Dalmatian on Pedigree.

Dm
Singing for the masses, rubber dinghy rapids,

I keep this rapping a habit and keep on fashioning magic.
B♭
I'm battling for respect, I don't know if I'll have it,

C   **C♯dim7**
This song's from the heart

(Dm)
Covers the planet, I'll take it back now.

Chorus 2   As Chorus 1

Verse 3

C♯dim7
I take it back now.

Dm
Now I don't ever want to be perfect,

'Cause I'm a singer that you never want to see shirtless.

B♭
And I ac - cept the fact that someone's gotta win worst-dressed,

C   **C♯dim7**
Taking my first steps into the scene, giving me focus.

Dm
Putting on a brave face, like Timothy Dalton,

Considering a name change, thinking it was hopeless.

B♭
Rhyming over recordings, avoiding tradition,

C
'Cause every days some lyrics and the melody could be written.

cont.

       Dm
Now absence can make your heart ache,

But drinking absinthe can change your mind-state, vividly,

Need to let my liver be.
B♭
  And I'll say it again,
              C   **C♯dim7**
Living life on the edge, with a close handful of friends,
                      Dm
It's good advice from the man that took his life on the road with me,

And I hope to see him blowing up globally,
                B♭
'Cause that's how it's supposed to be. I'm screaming out vocally,
            C   **N.C.**
It might seem totally impossible achieving life's dreams, but,
Dm
  But I just write schemes.

I'm never having a stylist, giving me tight jeans,
             B♭
Madison Square Garden is where I might be, but more likely
         C   **C♯dim7**
You find me in the back room of a dive bar with my mates
            Dm
Having a pint with McDaid, discussing records we made.

And every single second knowing that we'll never betray
             B♭
The way we were raised, remembering our background,
          C   **C♯dim7**
Sat down   that's how we plan it out; it's time to take it back now.

Chorus 3   As Chorus 1

Chorus 4

Dm
Mmm, come on and take it back love,

B♭   **C**   **C♯dim7** **Dm**
  Come on and take it back for us.

Don't you fade into the back love,

B♭   **C** **C♯dim7** **Dm**
  No._____

Tenerife Sea

Words & Music by Ed Sheeran, Johnny McDaid & Foy Vance

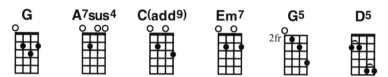

To match original recording, tune ukulele up one semitone

Intro | G   A7sus4 | C(add9) | G   A7sus4 | C(add9) |

| G   A7sus4 | C(add9) | G   A7sus4 | C(add9) |

| C(add9)   ‖

Verse 1

G   A7sus4   C(add9)
  You look so wonderful in your dress,

G   A7sus4   C(add9)
  I love your hair like that.

G   A7sus4   C(add9)
  The way it falls on the side of your neck,

Em7   G5   C(add9)
  Down your shoulders and back.

G   A7sus4   C(add9)
  We are sur - rounded by all of these lies

   G   A7sus4 C(add9)
And people who talk too much.

G   A7sus4 C(add9)
  You got the kind of look in your eyes

   Em7   G5   C(add9)
As if no one knows anything but us.

Pre-chorus 1

C5   G   G5
Should this be the last thing I see,

 C5   G   G5
I want you to know it's e - nough for me,

   C5   G   D5
'Cause all that you are is all that I'll ever need.

Chorus 1

(D5)   G   A⁷sus⁴ C(add⁹)   G   A⁷sus⁴ C(add⁹)

I'm so in love,   so in love,

     G   A⁷sus⁴ C(add⁹)   G   A⁷sus⁴ C(add⁹)

So in love,   so in love.

Verse 2

G   A⁷sus⁴ C(add⁹)

  You look so beautiful in this light,

G   A⁷sus⁴ C(add⁹)

  Your silhou - ette over me.

G   A⁷sus⁴   C(add⁹)

  The way it brings out the blue in your eyes

    Em⁷   G⁵   C(add⁹)

Is the Tenerife Sea.

   G   A⁷sus⁴   C(add⁹)

And all of the voices sur - rounding us here,

      G   A⁷sus⁴   C(add⁹)

They just fade out when you take a breath.

G   A⁷sus⁴   C(add⁹)

Just say the word and now we'll disappear

Em⁷   G⁵   C(add⁹)

Into the wilder - ness.

Pre-chorus 2   As Pre-chorus 1

Chorus 2   As Chorus 1

Bridge

Em⁷   C(add⁹) G   G⁵

Lumi - ère,   dar - ling,

Em⁷   C(add⁹) G

Lumi - ère over me.

Em⁷   C(add⁹) G   G⁵

Lumi - ère,   dar - ling,

Em⁷   C(add⁹) G

Lumi - ère over me.

Em⁷   C(add⁹) G   G⁵

Lumi - ère,   dar - ling,

Em⁷   C(add⁹) G

Lumi - ère over me.

Pre-chorus 3   As Pre-chorus 1

Chorus 3   As Chorus 1

| | G | A7sus4 | C(add9) |

Verse 3

G   **A7sus4   C(add9)**
You look so wonderful in your dress,

G   **A7sus4   C(add9)**
I love your hair like that.

G   **A7sus4   C(add9)**
And in a moment I knew you, Beth.

This

Words & Music by Ed Sheeran & Gordon Mills

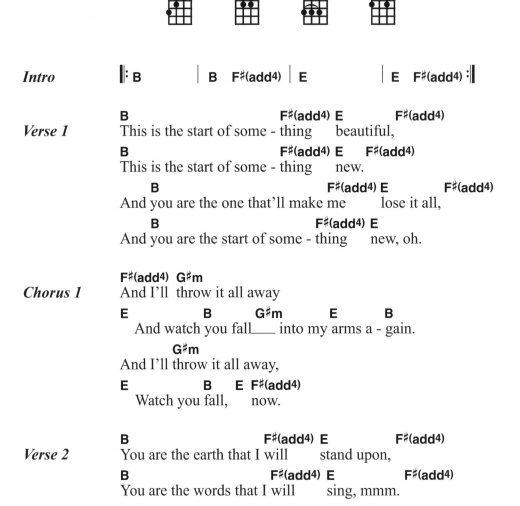

Intro ‖: B | B F#(add4) | E | E F#(add4) :‖

Verse 1

B   F#(add4) E   F#(add4)
This is the start of some - thing   beautiful,
B   F#(add4) E   F#(add4)
This is the start of some - thing   new.
        B   F#(add4) E   F#(add4)
And you are the one that'll make me   lose it all,
        B   F#(add4) E
And you are the start of some - thing   new, oh.

Chorus 1

F#(add4) G#m
And I'll throw it all away
E   B   G#m   E   B
   And watch you fall___ into my arms a - gain.
         G#m
And I'll throw it all away,
E   B   E F#(add4)
   Watch you fall,   now.

Verse 2

B   F#(add4) E   F#(add4)
You are the earth that I will   stand upon,
B   F#(add4) E   F#(add4)
You are the words that I will   sing, mmm.

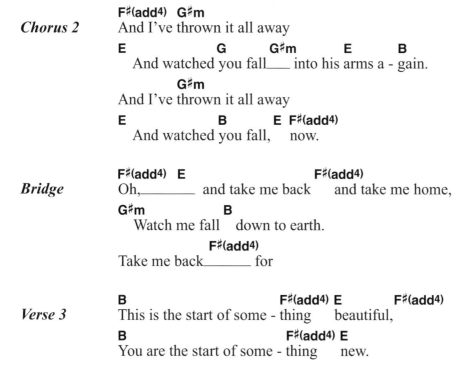

Chorus 2

F♯(add4) G♯m
And I've thrown it all away

E   G   G♯m   E   B
  And watched you fall__ into his arms a - gain.

           G♯m
And I've thrown it all away

E   B   E F♯(add4)
  And watched you fall,   now.

Bridge

F♯(add4) E   F♯(add4)
Oh,_____ and take me back   and take me home,

G♯m   B
  Watch me fall   down to earth.

           F♯(add4)
Take me back_____ for

Verse 3

B   F♯(add4) E   F♯(add4)
This is the start of some - thing   beautiful,

B   F♯(add4) E
You are the start of some - thing   new.

97

U.N.I

Words & Music by Ed Sheeran & Jake Gosling

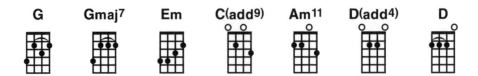

To match original recording, tune ukulele down one semitone

Verse 1

           G   Gmaj7 G
I found your hairband on my bedroom floor,

                                   Gmaj7   Em
The only evidence that you've been here be - fore.

                  C(add9)
And I don't get waves of missing you anymore,

G   Gmaj7
They're more like tsunami tides in my eyes.

                 G
Never getting dry, so I get high,

                         Gmaj7   G
Smoke away the days never sleep with the light on.

Weeks pass in the blink of an eye,

                        Gmaj7   Em
And I'm still drunk at the end of the night.

                         C(add9)
I don't drink like everybody else,

I do it to forget things about myself.

G
Stumble and fall with the head spin I got,

                     Gmaj7
My mind's with you but my heart's just not.

Pre-chorus 1

Am¹¹   C(add9)
So am I close to you any - more, if it's over,

Am¹¹   C(add9) D(add4)
And there's no chance that we'll work it out?_____

Chorus 1

(D)   G
That's why you and I ended over U.N.I.,

        Em   C(add9)   G
And I said that's fine, but you're the only one that knows I lied.

You and I ended over U.N.I.,

        Em   C(add9)   G   D G
And I said that's fine, but you're the only one that knows I lied.

Verse 2

N.C.   G
Everybody said we'd be together forever but I know that

I never wanna settle down,

Come around, break up the love like Lego now.
Em   C
Never wanna turn into another like you,

Sleep with my thoughts, dance with my views.
G
Everything's great but not everything's sure,

But you live in your halls and I live in a tour bus.

Now I'm in a position to be another stalker,

Like every thing I say seems to all sound awkward.

Like our last kiss it was perfect, we were nervous on the surface,
Em   C
And I'm always saying everyday that it was worth it,

Pain is only relevant if it still hurts.
      G
I for - get like an elephant, or we can use a sedative

And go back to the day we fell in love just on our first kiss.

Pre-chorus 2   As Pre-chorus 1

Chorus 2

(D) G
Oh, you and I ended over U.N.I.,

       Em   **C(add9)**   **G**
And I said that's fine, but you're the only one that knows I lied.

You and I ended over U.N.I.,

       Em   **C(add9)**   **G**
And I said that's fine, but you're the only one that knows I lied.

Link

G   **Em**   **C(add9) G**
Whoa, oh.

       Em C(add9)   **G**
Whoa, oh,   oh.____

Bridge

(G)   **Em**   **C(add9)**   **G**
Because   if I was gonna go somewhere,   I'd be there by now

Am11   **C(add9)**
And maybe I can let myself   down, whoa.

Em   **C(add9)**   **G**
And I'm thinking that I'm unaware,

                                    Am11
I keep my feet on the ground and keep   looking around

                       C(add9)
To make sure I'm not the only one to feel low.

           Em   **C(add9)**   **G**   **D(add4)**
Because if you   want, I'll take you in my arms

                 Em   **C(add9)**   **G**   **D(add4)**
And keep you shel - tered from all that I've done wrong.

               Em   **C(add9) G**   **D(add4)**
And I'll know you'll say that I'm the on - ly one,

        Am11
But I know   God made another one of me

   C(add9)   **D(add4)**
To love you better than I ever will.

Chorus 3
$\qquad$ **G**
’Cause you and I ended over U.N.I.,
$\qquad$ **Em** $\qquad$ **C(add9)** $\qquad\qquad\qquad\qquad$ **G**
And I said that’s fine, but you’re the only one that knows I lied.

You and I ended over U.N.I.,
$\qquad$ **Em** $\qquad$ **C(add9)** $\qquad\qquad\qquad\qquad$ **G** $\qquad$ **D G**
And I said that’s fine, but you’re the only one that knows I lied.

Wake Me Up

Words & Music by Ed Sheeran & Jake Gosling

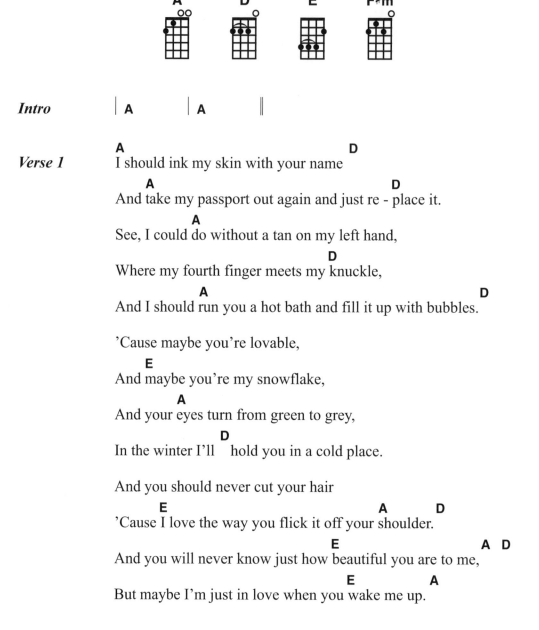

Intro | **A** | **A** ||

Verse 1

A
I should ink my skin with your name   **D**

  A   **D**
And take my passport out again and just re - place it.

               A
See, I could do without a tan on my left hand,

                        D
Where my fourth finger meets my knuckle,

            A   **D**
And I should run you a hot bath and fill it up with bubbles.

'Cause maybe you're lovable,

     E
And maybe you're my snowflake,

          A
And your eyes turn from green to grey,

              D
In the winter I'll   hold you in a cold place.

And you should never cut your hair

        E   **A**   **D**
'Cause I love the way you flick it off your shoulder.

                        E   **A D**
And you will never know just how beautiful you are to me,

                      E   **A**
But maybe I'm just in love when you wake me up.

Verse 2

    A
And would you ever feel guilty if you did the same to me,
    D   E
   Could you make me a cup of   tea to open my eyes in the right way?
    A
   And I know you love Shrek 'cause we've watched it twelve times,
    D   E
   But maybe you're hoping for a fairy tale too.
            A
And if your DVD breaks today, you should've got a VCR,
    D   E
   Because I've never owned a Blu-ray, true say.
         A
And now I've always been shit at computer games,

And your brother always beats me,
      D   E
And if I lost, I'd go across and chuck all the controllers at the TV.
      A
And then you'd laugh at me and be asking me

If I'm gonna be home next week.
         D
And then you'd lie with me till I fall asleep
     E
And flutter eyelash on my cheek between the sheets.
    D   E   A D
   And you will never know just how beautiful you are to me,
                  E   A
But maybe I'm just in love when you wake me up.

Verse 3

A
And I think you hate the smell of smoke,

You must try to get me to stop,
D   E
   But you drink as much as me   and I get drunk a lot.
A   D
   So I take you to the beach and walk along the sand,___
D   E
And I'll make you a heart   pendant with a pebble held in my hand.
A
   And I'll carve it like a necklace so the heart falls where your chest is.
D
   And now a piece of me is a piece of the beach,
E   A
   And it falls just where it needs to be and rests   peacefully,

So you just need to breathe
                            D   E
To feel my heart against yours now, against yours now.
    D   E   F♯m A
'Cause maybe I'm just in love when you wake me up.
    D   E   F♯m A
Or maybe I'm just in love when you wake me up.
D   E   A
Maybe I fell in love when you woke me up.

You Need Me, I Don't Need You

Words & Music by Ed Sheeran

Em **Gmaj⁷** **Asus⁴** **C** **D** **G** **A**

Intro | Em | Em | Em | Em   ‖

Verse 1

Em
Now I'm in town, break it down, thinking of making a new sound,
Gmaj⁷
Playing a different show every night in front of a new crowd.
Asus⁴
That's you now, ciao, seems that life is great now,
C   **D**
See me lose focus, as I sing to you loud.
Em   **Gmaj⁷**
And I can't, no, I won't hush,
                          Asus⁴
I'll say the words that make you blush,
              C **D**
I'm gonna sing this now.   Oh, oh.

Verse 2

Em
  See, I'm true, my songs are where my heart is,
G
  I'm like glue, I stick to other artists.
A
  I'm not you, now that would be disastrous,
C   **D**
Let me sing and do my thing and move to greener pastures.
Em
  See, I'm real, I do it all, it's all me,
G
  I'm not fake, don't ever call me lazy.
A
  I won't stay put, give me the chance to be free,
C   **D**
Suffolk sadly seems to sort of suffocate me.

Chorus 1

Em   G
   'Cause you need me, man, I don't need you,

                    A
You need me, man, I don't need you,

                    C
You need me, man, I don't need you at all,

       D   Em
You need me, man, I don't need you.

                    G
You need me, man, I don't need you,

                    A
You need me, man, I don't need you,

                    C
You need me, man, I don't need you at all,

      D
You need me.

Verse 3

(D)   Em
I sing, I write my own tune and I write my own verse,

     G
Hell,   don't need another word-smith to make my tune sell.

A
Call yourself a singer-writer, you're just bluffing,

     C   D
Your name's on the credits and you didn't write nothing.

Em
   I sing fast, I know that all my shit's cool,

G
   I will blast and I didn't go to Brit School.

A
   I came fast with the way I act, right,

N.C.
   I can't last if I'm smoking on a crack pipe.

Verse 4

    Em
   And I won't be a product of my genre,

      G
My mind will always be stronger than my songs are.

A
Never believe the bullshit that fake guys feed to ya,

C   **D**
Always read the stories that you hear on Wikipedia.

Em
   And musically I'm demonstrating,

G
When I perform live, feels like I am meditating.

A
Times at the Enterprise when some fella filmed me,

   C   **D**
A young singer-writer like Gabriella Cilmi.

Chorus 2   As Chorus 1

Verse 5

    (D)   **Em**
'Cause with the lyrics I'll be aiming it right,

                    Gmaj7
I won't stop till my name's in lights

At stadium heights with Damien Rice.

       Asus4
On red carpets, now I'm on Arabian Nights,

          C   **D**
Because I'm young I know my brother's gonna give me advice.

     Em
Long nighter, short height and I gone hyper,

Gmaj7
Never be anything but a singer-songwriter, yeah.

Asus4
   The game's over but now I'm on a new level,

C   **D**
Watch how I step on the track without a loop pedal.

Verse 6	**Em**
	People think that I'm bound to blow up,
	
	   G
	I've done around about a thousand shows,
	
	   A
	But I haven't got a house plus I live on a couch,
	
	  C **D** **Em**
	So you believe the lyrics when I'm singing them out, wow.
	
	                G
	From day one, I've been prepared with VO5 wax for my ginger hair,
	
	     A **C**
	So now I'm back to the sofa, giving a dose of what the future holds,
	
	       D
	'Cause it's an - other day.

Verse 7
 	
cont.
	(D) **Em**
	Plus I'll keep my last name forever, keep this genre pretty basic,
	
	     G
	Gonna be breaking into other people's tunes when I chase it
	
	     A
	And re - place it with the elephant in the room with a facelift,
	
	C **D**
	Into another rapper's shoes using new laces.
	
	            Em
	I'm selling CDs from my rucksack aiming for the papers,
	
	     G
	Selling CDs from my rucksack aiming for the majors.
	
	     A
	Nation - wide tour with Just Jack, still had to get the bus back,
	
	C **D**
	Clean cut kid without a razor for the mustache.

Verse 8

Em
I hit back when the pen hurts me,

    G
I'm still a choir boy in a Fenchurch tee,

      A
I'm still the same as a year ago, but more people hear me though,

   C   D
Ac - cording to the MySpace and YouTube videos.

     Em
I'm always doing shows if I'm not I'm in the studio,

G
Truly broke, never growing up call me Rufio.

A
Melody music maker reading all the papers,

     C   N.C.
They say I'm up and coming like I'm fucking in an elevator.

Chorus 3

Em   G
  'Cause you need me, man, I don't need you,

                 A
You need me, man, I don't need you,

                 C
You need me, man, I don't need you at all,

      D   Em
You need me, man, I don't need you.

                 G
You need me, man, I don't need you,

                 A
You need me, man, I don't need you,

                 C
You need me, man, I don't need you at all,

      D   N.C.
You need me, man, I don't need you.

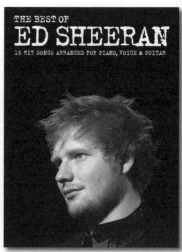
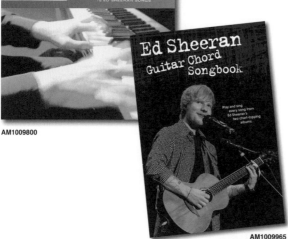

Whatever you want...

Music Sales publishes the very best in printed music for ukulele. Our books cover all levels of playing and all styles of music including rock & pop, jazz, blues and country.

Many of our practical publications come with helpful CDs or exclusive download links to music files for backing tracks and other audio extras.

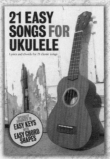

We also publish a large variety of tuition books so you can teach yourself how to play, and ukulele resources for teachers.

So, whatever you want, Music Sales has it.

Just visit your local music shop and ask to see our huge range of music in print.

In case of difficulty, contact
marketing@musicsales.co.uk

Tuning your ukulele

The ukulele is unusual among string instruments in that the strings are not tuned in order of pitch. Watch out for this!
Here are the tuning notes for a ukulele on a piano keyboard:

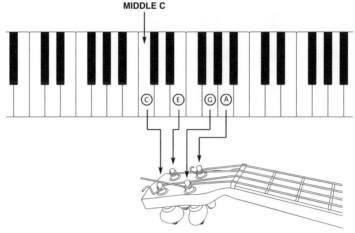

A good way to remember the notes of the ukulele's strings is this little tune:

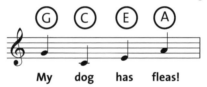

My   dog   has   fleas!

Reading chord boxes

Chord boxes are diagrams of the ukulele neck viewed head upwards, face on as illustrated. The top horizontal line is the nut, unless a higher fret number is indicated, the others are the frets.

The vertical lines are the strings, starting from G (or 4th) on the left to A (or 1st) on the right.

The black dots indicate where to place your fingers.

Strings marked with an O are played open, not fretted. Strings marked with an X should not be played.

The curved bracket indicates a 'barre' – hold down the strings under the bracket with your first finger, using your fingers to fret the remaining notes.

N.C. = No chord.

Am

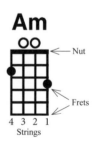

G

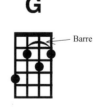